TABLES EXPERT B

Alison MacMahon

g
GILL

Preface

Tables Expert is a new series of full-colour tables activity books. *Tables Expert* **A** and **B** cover **addition** and **subtraction** tables, while *Tables Expert* C and D cover multiplication and division tables. *Tables Expert* links the learning of mathematical tables to many strands and strand units of the maths curriculum, with a strong emphasis on problem-solving. This allows children to condolidate their tables by application to real mathematical problems and to a wide number of mathematical strands and strand units.

How to use this book

Learn
A unit covers a week's learning; new material and activities are introduced on **Mondays**, **Tuesdays** and **Wednesdays**.

Revise
The **Thursday** page in each unit revises and consolidates the new work covered from Monday to Wednesday and applies the week's table to problem-solving activities.

Continuous assessment
Friday is a test day. The last line on the Thursday page of each unit directs the children to the corresponding test page, e.g. 'Do test 1 on page 118'. **Revision assessments** are also provided after each revision unit. Pupils can **record a summary** of their Friday test scores at the back of the book.

Further revision
There are **regular look-back units** throughout the books in addition to the Thursday revision page in each unit.

Series features

Look, say, cover, write, check
Here is a quick overview of how look, say, cover, write, check works:

- **Look:** Look at the table.
- **Say:** Say the table out loud.
- **Cover:** Cover the table.
- **Write:** Write the complete table (while it's covered).
- **Check:** Check if what you wrote down is correct!

Self-assessment
How did you do? 😊 ● 😐 ● 😞 ●

Each Thursday page contains a self-assessment section for children to **assess their learning** from the week in advance of their Friday test.

Problem-solving
A **RUCSAC** icon (read, understand, choose, solve, answer, check) is included to remind pupils of the rules associated with problem-solving in maths. **Rough work** areas are also provided to encourage their use for calculations.

Mata sa Rang/Maths recovery
Mata sa Rang/**Maths recovery** strategies have been included to enhance pupils' knowledge and understanding of key aspects of the number strand in maths in conjunction with learning mathematical tables.

Language of maths/Maths vocabulary

Throughout *Tables Expert* there is a key focus on learning and understanding the correct mathematical language associated with each mathematical operation. For example: words such as 'and', 'plus', 'altogether', 'all' and 'add' mean ADD, etc.

Visual Number Line
The visual number line at the beginning of each unit assists pupils in identifying number patterns and combinations.

> **Tips!**
> - The relevant table should be practised daily.
> - Each day's work with tables should ideally take 10–15 minutes.
> - Black and white artworks are included throughout the book to provide additional colouring extension exercises.

Gill Education
Hume Avenue
Park West
Dublin 12
www.gilleducation.ie

Gill Education is an imprint of M.H. Gill & Co.

© Alison MacMahon 2016

All rights reserved. No part of this publication may be copied, reproduced or transmitted in any form or by any means without written permission of the publishers or else under the terms of any licence permitting limited copying issued by the Irish Copyright Licensing Agency.

Design and layout: Outburst Design

Illustrators: Derry Dillon and Maria Murray

Cover design: Aisli Madden

ISBN: 978-0-7171-69627

Any links to external websites should not be construed as an endorsement by Gill & Macmillan of the content or view of the linked material. Furthermore it cannot be guaranteed that all external links will be live.

For permission to reproduce photographs, the authors and publisher gratefully acknowledge the following: Freepik.com

The authors and publisher have made every effort to trace all copyright holders, but if any has been inadvertently overlooked we would be pleased to make the necessary arrangement at the first opportunity.

Contents

Week	Operations	Strands and Strand Units		Page
		Number	Measures	
1	+ 1	Counting and numeration	Money	4
2	+ 2	Counting and numeration	Money	7
3	+ 3	Counting and numeration	Money	10
4	+ 4	Counting and numeration	Money	13
5	Revision: + 1, + 2, + 3, + 4	Counting and numeration		16
6	+ 5	Counting and numeration	Money	19
7	+ 6	Counting and numeration	Money	22
8	+ 7	Counting and numeration	Money	25
9	+ 8	Counting and numeration	Money	28
10	Revision: + 5, + 6, + 7, + 8	Counting and numeration	Weight, Length	31
11	+ 9	Counting and numeration	Money, Length	34
12	+ 10	Counting and numeration	Money	37
13	+ 11	Counting and numeration	Money	40
14	+ 12	Counting and numeration	Length, Money	43
15	Revision: + 9, + 10, + 11, + 12	Counting and numeration	Weight, Length	46
16	– 1	Counting and numeration	Money	49
17	– 2	Counting and numeration	Money	52
18	– 3	Counting and numeration	Money	55
19	– 4	Counting and numeration	Money	58
20	Revision: – 1, – 2, – 3, – 4	Counting and numeration	Length, Weight	61
21	– 5	Counting and numeration	Time, Money	64
22	– 6	Counting and numeration	Money	67
23	– 7	Counting and numeration	Money	70
24	– 8	Counting and numeration	Money	73
25	Revision: – 5, – 6, – 7, – 8	Counting and numeration	Length	76
26	– 9	Counting and numeration	Time, Money	79
27	– 10	Counting and numeration	Money	82
28	– 11	Counting and numeration	Money	85
29	– 12	Counting and numeration	Money	88
30	Revision: – 9, – 10, – 11, – 12	Counting and numeration	Length	91
Friday Tests				94
Revision Tests				100
Friday Test Results				103

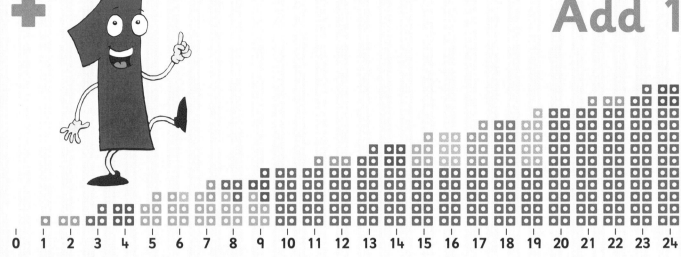

Add 1

0 1 2 3 4 5 6 7 8 9 10 11 12 13 14 15 16 17 18 19 20 21 22 23 24

Monday

+ 1 Tables

Monday	0 + 1 =	1
	1 + 1 =	2
	2 + 1 =	3
	3 + 1 =	4
	4 + 1 =	5
	5 + 1 =	6
Tuesday	6 + 1 =	7
	7 + 1 =	8
	8 + 1 =	9
	9 + 1 =	10
Wednesday	10 + 1 =	11
	11 + 1 =	12
	12 + 1 =	13

Look

Say

Cover

Write

Check

Learn these

0 + 1 = 1
1 + 1 = 2
2 + 1 = 3
3 + 1 = 4
4 + 1 = 5

You try!

0 + 1 =
1 + 1 =
2 + 1 =
3 + 1 =
4 + 1 =

1 Count on

(a) 2 and 1 =

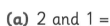 0 +

(b) 0 and 1 =

(c) 1 and 1 =

(d) 3 and 1 =

2 Colour the correct sum

(a) +

| 3 + 1 = 4 | or | 0 + 4 = 4 | or | 4 + 0 = 4 |

(b) +

| 5 + 0 = 5 | or | 4 + 1 = 5 | or | 3 + 2 = 5 |

3 Correct these.

✓ or ✗

(a) 3 + 1 = 4

(b) 1 + 1 = 2

(c) 2 + 1 = 1

(d) 4 + 1 = 5

(e) 0 + 1 = 1

Strand: Number **Strand Unit:** Counting and numeration; Operations – addition.

Tuesday

Learn these

5 + 1 = 6
6 + 1 = 7
7 + 1 = 8
8 + 1 = 9

You try!

5 + 1 =
6 + 1 =
7 + 1 =
8 + 1 =

1 Addition sums

(a) 3	(b) 5	(c) 8	(d) 6	(e) 1
+ 1	+ 1	+ 1	+ 1	+ 1

(f) 7	(g) 0	(h) 4	(i) 2	(j) 9
+ 1	+ 1	+ 1	+ 1	+ 1

2 Count on 1

(a) 5 →
(b) 8 →
(c) 7 →
(d) 6 →
(e) 4 →

3 Add up

(a) What is 8 and 1?
(b) What is 5 and 1?
(c) What is 6 and 1?
(d) What is 9 and 1?
(e) What is 7 and 1?

Wednesday

Learn these

9 + 1 = 10
10 + 1 = 11
11 + 1 = 12
12 + 1 = 13

You try!

9 + 1 =
10 + 1 =
11 + 1 =
12 + 1 =

1 Fill in the missing numbers

(a) 9 +   = 10
(b)   + 1 = 12
(c) 10 +   = 11
(d)   + 1 = 13

2 + or – ?

(a) 9   1 = 10
(b) 11   1 = 10
(c) 12   1 = 13
(d) 10   1 = 9
(e) 8   1 = 7

3 Correct these. ✓ or ✗

(a) 12 + 1 = 13
(b) 10 + 1 = 9
(c) 9 + 1 = 0
(d) 11 + 1 = 12

4 Adding money

How much altogether?

c

Strand: Number **Strand Unit:** Counting and numeration; Operations – addition
Strand: Measures **Strand Unit:** Money.

Thursday Revision and Problem-solving

Learn these

0 + 1 =	1
1 + 1 =	2
2 + 1 =	3
3 + 1 =	4
4 + 1 =	5
5 + 1 =	6
6 + 1 =	7
7 + 1 =	8
8 + 1 =	9
9 + 1 =	10
10 + 1 =	11
11 + 1 =	12
12 + 1 =	13

❶ Problem-solving with tables

Colour each matching problem and sum the same colour. Write the answer.

(a) Alex has **3** pets. Jay has **1** pet. How many pets do Alex and Jay have altogether?

(b) John has **4** cent. His dad gives him **1** cent. How much money does John have now?

(c) A lady bought **5** apples. Then she bought **1** more apple. How many apples does she have now?

(d) Jessica's hens laid **7** eggs. Then Jessica found **1** more egg. How many eggs are there altogether?

5 + 1 =
3 + 1 = 4
7 + 1 =
4 + 1 =

❷ Colour 'yes' or 'no'

(a) 3 + 1 = 4   [yes] [no]

(b) 1 + 1 = 2   [yes] [no]

(c) 7 + 1 = 8   [yes] [no]

(d) 5 + 1 = 4   [yes] [no]

❸ Addition words

Learn the words below. These words tell us to <u>add</u>.

[add] [and] [plus] [all]

[altogether] [total] [sum of]

Rough work

❹ Test yourself!

2 + 1 =	8 + 1 =	10 + 1 =
12 + 1 =	1 + 1 =	5 + 1 =
3 + 1 =	7 + 1 =	6 + 1 =
9 + 1 =	11 + 1 =	
0 + 1 =	4 + 1 =	

My score [ ] / 13

How did you do?

Strand: Number **Strand Unit:** Counting and numeration; Operations – addition
Strand: Measures **Strand Unit:** Money **Skill:** Problem-solving.

Do Test 1 on page 94.

Add 2

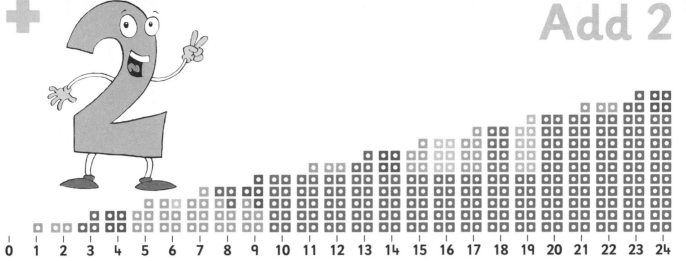

| 0 | 1 | 2 | 3 | 4 | 5 | 6 | 7 | 8 | 9 | 10 | 11 | 12 | 13 | 14 | 15 | 16 | 17 | 18 | 19 | 20 | 21 | 22 | 23 | 24 |

Monday

+ 2 Tables

Monday

0 + 2 = 2
1 + 2 = 3
2 + 2 = 4
3 + 2 = 5
4 + 2 = 6
5 + 2 = 7

Tuesday

6 + 2 = 8
7 + 2 = 9
8 + 2 = 10

Wednesday

9 + 2 = 11
10 + 2 = 12
11 + 2 = 13
12 + 2 = 14

Look · **Say** · **Cover** · **Write** · **Check**

Learn these

0 + 2 = 2
1 + 2 = 3
2 + 2 = 4
3 + 2 = 5
4 + 2 = 6

You try!

0 + 2 =

1 + 2 =

2 + 2 =

3 + 2 =

4 + 2 =

1 Add 2

Match each number with the correct answer.

+ 2

3	9
7	5
10	2
12	13
0	12
6	14
9	11
2	8
11	4

2 Problem-solving with tables – pet shop

Below are the animals in a pet shop. Answer the questions that follow.

(a) How many dogs and cats?   3 + 1 = 4

(b) How many dogs and frogs?

(c) How many goldfish and rabbits?

(d) How many dogs and rabbits?

(e) How many dogs and rabbits and frogs?

Don't forget your... RUCSAC!

Strand: Number **Strand Unit:** Counting and numeration; Operations – addition **Skill:** Problem-solving.

Tuesday

Learn these

5 + 2 = 7
6 + 2 = 8
7 + 2 = 9
8 + 2 = 10

You try!

5 + 2 =

6 + 2 =

7 + 2 =

8 + 2 =

❶ Ring the correct answer

(a) 6 + 2 = 4 or 8

(b) 5 + 2 = 7 or 3

(c) 8 + 2 = 7 or 10

(d) 7 + 2 = 11 or 9

❷ Count on 2

(a) 5 → 7   (b) 7 →

(c) 3 →   (d) 4 →

(e) 8 →   (f) 6 →

(g) 0 →   (h) 2 →

❸ Finish the number sentences

(a) 1 + 2 =   (b) 7 + 2 =

(c) 3 + 2 =   (d) 4 + 2 =

(e) 6 + 2 =   (f) 2 + 2 =

(g) 5 + 2 =   (h) 9 + 2 =

(i) 8 + 2 =   (j) 10 + 2 =

Wednesday

Learn these

9 + 2 = 11
10 + 2 = 12
11 + 2 = 13
12 + 2 = 14

You try!

9 + 2 =

10 + 2 =

11 + 2 =

12 + 2 =

❶ Add up

(a) 2 + 3 + 2 =

(b) 4 + 2 + 2 =

❷ Colour ✓ or ✗

(a) 9 + 2 = 11   ✓ ✗

(b) 10 + 2 = 8   ✓ ✗

(c) 12 + 2 = 14   ✓ ✗

(d) 11 + 2 = 13   ✓ ✗

(e) 8 + 2 = 12   ✓ ✗

❸ Sums with brackets

(a) (6 + 3) + 2 =

(b) (9 + 2) + 2 =

(c) (11 + 2) + 0 =

(d) (12 + 2) + 3 =

(e) (8 + 2) + 1 =

Strand: Number **Strand Unit:** Counting and numeration; Operations – addition.

Thursday Revision and Problem-solving

Learn these

$0 + 2 = 2$
$1 + 2 = 3$
$2 + 2 = 4$
$3 + 2 = 5$
$4 + 2 = 6$
$5 + 2 = 7$
$6 + 2 = 8$
$7 + 2 = 9$
$8 + 2 = 10$
$9 + 2 = 11$
$10 + 2 = 12$
$11 + 2 = 13$
$12 + 2 = 14$

1 Colour the correct sum

(a)

| $2 + 2 = 4$ | or | $5 + 2 = 7$ | or | $4 + 5 = 9$ |

(b)

| $2 + 2 = 4$ | or | $0 + 5 = 5$ | or | $3 + 2 = 5$ |

Rough work

2 + or – word?

(a) add   +

(b) plus

(c) subtract

(d) altogether

(e) total

(f) all

(g) minus

3 Problem-solving with tables

Write a number sentence to match each problem.

Don't forget your... RUCSAC!

(a) A bar costs **10** cent. A lollipop costs **2** cent. How much do they cost altogether?		$10 + 2 = 12$
(b) **8** children were at a party. **2** more arrived. How many children are at the party now?		
(c) A farmer has **10** sheep and **2** cows. How many animals does she have in total?		
(d) Alan had **9** stickers. He bought **2** more. How many stickers does he have now?		

4 Test yourself!

$2 + 2 =$	$8 + 2 =$	$10 + 2 =$
$12 + 2 =$	$1 + 2 =$	$5 + 2 =$
$3 + 2 =$	$7 + 2 =$	$6 + 2 =$
$9 + 2 =$	$11 + 2 =$	
$0 + 2 =$	$4 + 2 =$	

My score   / 13

How did you do?

Strand: Number **Strand Unit:** Counting and numeration; Operations – addition
Strand: Measures **Strand Unit:** Money **Skill:** Problem-solving.

Do Test 2 on page 94.   9

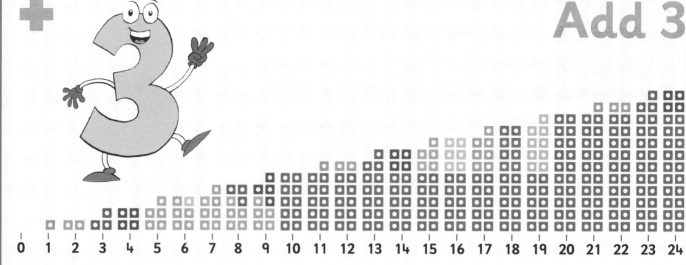

Add 3

| 0 | 1 | 2 | 3 | 4 | 5 | 6 | 7 | 8 | 9 | 10 | 11 | 12 | 13 | 14 | 15 | 16 | 17 | 18 | 19 | 20 | 21 | 22 | 23 | 24 |

Monday

+ 3 Tables

Monday	
0 + 3 =	3
1 + 3 =	4
2 + 3 =	5
3 + 3 =	6
4 + 3 =	7
5 + 3 =	8
6 + 3 =	9
7 + 3 =	10
8 + 3 =	11
9 + 3 =	12
10 + 3 =	13
11 + 3 =	14
12 + 3 =	15

Monday
Tuesday
Wednesday

Look
Say
Cover
Write
Check

Learn these

0 + 3 = 3
1 + 3 = 4
2 + 3 = 5
3 + 3 = 6
4 + 3 = 7

You try!

0 + 3 =

1 + 3 =

2 + 3 =

3 + 3 =

4 + 3 =

1 Count on

(a)  + 3 =

(b)  + 3 =

(c) 0 +  =

(d)  + 3 =

(e) 4 +  =

2 Adding money

(a) and

equals ____ cent

(b) +

makes ____ cent

(c) and

= ____ cent

(d)  +

is the same as ____ cent

Strand: Number Strand Unit: Counting and numeration; Operations – addition
Strand: Measures Strand Unit: Money.

Tuesday

Learn these

5 + 3 = 8
6 + 3 = 9
7 + 3 = 10
8 + 3 = 11

You try!

5 + 3 =
6 + 3 =
7 + 3 =
8 + 3 =

1 Addition sums

(a)	(b)	(c)	(d)	(e)
7 + 3	5 + 3	8 + 3	6 + 3	1 + 3

(f)	(g)	(h)	(i)	(j)
3 + 3	0 + 3	10 + 3	9 + 3	12 + 3

2 Fill in the missing numbers

(a)  and  = _____ frogs

(b) and _____ flowers =

(c) and _____ pencils =

Wednesday

Learn these

9 + 3 = 12
10 + 3 = 13
11 + 3 = 14
12 + 3 = 15

You try!

9 + 3 =
10 + 3 =
11 + 3 =
12 + 3 =

1 Fill in the missing numbers

(a) 9 + _____ = 12
(b) _____ + 3 = 14
(c) 10 + _____ = 13
(d) _____ + 3 = 15

2 + or – ?

(a) 9 ___ 3 = 12
(b) 11 ___ 3 = 8
(c) 12 ___ 3 = 15
(d) 10 ___ 3 = 7
(e) 8 ___ 3 = 11

3 Count on 3

(a) 5 →
(b) 8 →
(c) 7 →
(d) 6 →
(e) 9 →

4 Correct these. ✓ or ✗

(a) 5 + 3 = 8
(b) 7 + 3 = 10
(c) 8 + 3 = 12
(d) 6 + 3 = 9
(e) 10 + 3 = 15

Strand: Number **Strand Unit:** Counting and numeration; Operations – addition.

Thursday Revision and Problem-solving

Learn these

0	+	3	=	3
1	+	3	=	4
2	+	3	=	5
3	+	3	=	6
4	+	3	=	7
5	+	3	=	8
6	+	3	=	9
7	+	3	=	10
8	+	3	=	11
9	+	3	=	12
10	+	3	=	13
11	+	3	=	14
12	+	3	=	15

1 Problem-solving with tables

Colour each matching problem and sum the same colour. Write the answer.

Don't forget your... RUCSAC!

(a) Shane has **5** cent. His mam gives him **3** cent. How much money does Shane have now?

4 + 3 =

(b) Harry has **4** marbles. His friend gives him **3** more. How many marbles does Harry have now?

7 + 3 =

(c) Ciara has **7** sweets. Her aunt gives her **3** more. How many sweets does Ciara have now?

5 + 3 =

2 Fill in the missing numbers

(a)   and  = ducks

(b)   and trees =

(c)   and pencils =

Rough work

3 Test yourself!

2 + 3 =	8 + 3 =	10 + 3 =
12 + 3 =	1 + 3 =	5 + 3 =
3 + 3 =	7 + 3 =	6 + 3 =
9 + 3 =	11 + 3 =	
0 + 3 =	4 + 3 =	

How did you do?

My score ___ / 13

Strand: Number **Strand Unit:** Counting and numeration; Operations – addition
Strand: Measures **Strand Unit:** Money **Skill:** Problem-solving.

Do Test 3 on page 94.

Add 4

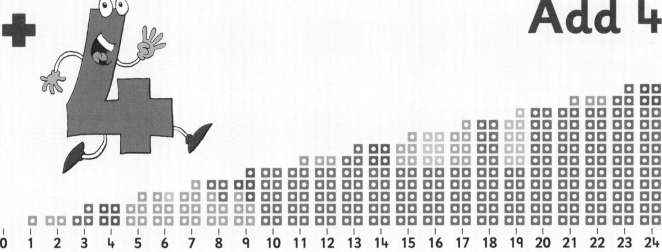

0 1 2 3 4 5 6 7 8 9 10 11 12 13 14 15 16 17 18 19 20 21 22 23 24

Monday

+ 4 Tables

Monday	0 + 4 = 4
	1 + 4 = 5
	2 + 4 = 6
	3 + 4 = 7
	4 + 4 = 8
	5 + 4 = 9
Tuesday	6 + 4 = 10
	7 + 4 = 11
	8 + 4 = 12
	9 + 4 = 13
Wednesday	10 + 4 = 14
	11 + 4 = 15
	12 + 4 = 16

Look

Say

Cover

Write

Check

Learn these

0 + 4 = 4
1 + 4 = 5
2 + 4 = 6
3 + 4 = 7
4 + 4 = 8

You try!

0 + 4 =

1 + 4 =

2 + 4 =

3 + 4 =

4 + 4 =

1 Add up

(a)  + 4 =

(b) 0 +  =

(c)  + 4 =

(d)  + 4 =

(e) + 4 =

2 Fill in the missing numbers

(a)  + [ ] = 7

(b) [ ] +  = 8

(c) [ ] +  = 4

3 Plus 4

+ 4

(a) 1 [5]

(b) 0 [ ]

(c) 4 [ ]

(d) 2 [ ]

(e) 3 [ ]

Tuesday

Learn these

5 + 4 = 9
6 + 4 = 10
7 + 4 = 11
8 + 4 = 12

You try!

5 + 4 =

6 + 4 =

7 + 4 =

8 + 4 =

1 Addition sums

(a) 5 + 4 =

(b) 8 + 4 =

(c) 3 + 4 =

(d) 0 + 4 =

(e) 7 + 4 =

(f) 2 + 4 =

(g) 4 + 4 =

(h) 1 + 4 =

(i) 12 + 4 =

(j) 10 + 4 =

2 Fill in the missing numbers

(a) 5 +   = 9

(b)   + 8 = 12

(c) 6 +   = 10

(d)   + 4 = 11

3 Correct these. ✓ or ✗

(a) 7 + 4 = 11

(b) 0 + 4 = 0

(c) 5 + 4 = 9

(d) 8 + 4 = 12

Wednesday

Learn these

9 + 4 = 13
10 + 4 = 14
11 + 4 = 15
12 + 4 = 16

You try!

9 + 4 =

10 + 4 =

11 + 4 =

12 + 4 =

1 + or – ?

(a) 9   4 = 13

(b) 11   4 = 7

(c) 12   4 = 16

(d) 10   4 = 6

(e) 8   4 = 12

3 Sums with brackets

(a) (7 + 4) + 2 =

(b) (5 + 0) + 4 =

(c) (11 + 4) + 3 =

(d) (12 + 3) + 4 =

2 Add 4

Match each number with the correct answer.

+ 4

3	11
7	7
10	4
12	15
0	14
6	16
9	13
2	10
11	6

Strand: Number **Strand Unit:** Counting and numeration; Operations – addition.

Thursday — Revision and Problem-solving

Learn these

0 + 4 = 4
1 + 4 = 5
2 + 4 = 6
3 + 4 = 7
4 + 4 = 8
5 + 4 = 9
6 + 4 = 10
7 + 4 = 11
8 + 4 = 12
9 + 4 = 13
10 + 4 = 14
11 + 4 = 15
12 + 4 = 16

1 Problem-solving with tables

Colour the sum that matches each problem.

Don't forget your... RUCSAC!

(a) A sweet costs **10** cent. A lollipop costs **4** cent. How much do they cost altogether?

| 10 + 10 = 20 | or | 10 + 4 = 14 |

(b) A pet shop owner had **11** mice. He sold **4** mice. How many mice does he have now?

| 11 + 4 = 15 | or | 11 − 4 = 7 |

(c) A farmer had **12** cows. He bought **4** more at the mart. How many cows does he have now?

| 12 + 4 = 16 | or | 12 − 4 = 8 |

2 Add and draw

(a)	and		is the same as	
(b)	add		=	
(c)	plus		equals	

Rough work

4 Test yourself!

12 + 4 =	6 + 4 =	9 + 4 =
2 + 4 =	11 + 4 =	10 + 4 =
1 + 4 =	0 + 4 =	8 + 4 =
3 + 4 =	7 + 4 =	
4 + 4 =	5 + 4 =	My score ___ / 13

How did you do?

Strand: Number **Strand Unit:** Counting and numeration; Operations – addition
Strand: Measures **Strand Unit:** Money **Skill:** Problem-solving.

Do Test 4 on page 94.   15

Revision and Problem-solving

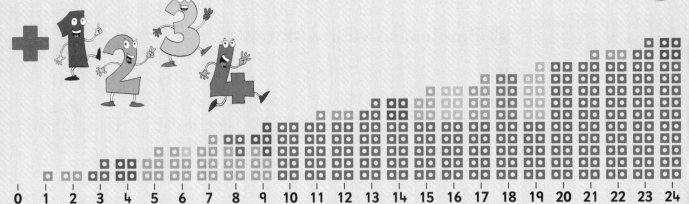

```
0   1   2   3   4   5   6   7   8   9   10  11  12  13  14  15  16  17  18  19  20  21  22  23  24
```

1 Test your memory!

Finish these number sentences.

(a) 6 + 1 =	**(b)** 8 + 3 =	**(c)** 5 + 2 =
(d) 7 + 4 =	**(e)** 9 + 1 =	**(f)** 4 + 4 =
(g) 2 + 2 =	**(h)** 10 + 1 =	**(i)** 12 + 3 =
(j) 8 + 2 =	**(k)** 11 + 4 =	**(l)** 12 + 1 =
(m) 7 + 2 =	**(n)** 8 + 4 =	**(o)** 11 + 1 =
(p) 9 + 2 =	**(q)** 3 + 3 =	**(r)** 12 + 4 =

2 Find the total

(a) 4 + 3 =

(b) 6 + 2 =

3 Crack the code!

Complete the number sentences to crack the code.

1 + 1 = **g**	8 + 3 = **o**
7 + 2 = **e**	9 + 4 = **k**
2 + 3 = **r**	2 + 2 = **t**
11 + 4 = **w**	9 + 3 = **a**

☐ ☐ ☐ ☐ ☐   ☐ ☐ ☐ ☐ !

2   5   9   12   4   15   11   5   13

4 Fill in the missing numbers

(a)	(b)	(c)	(d)	(e)	(f)	(g)
9	12	3	0	5	7	10
+ 4	+ ☐	+ ☐	+ 2	+ ☐	+ 3	+ ☐
☐	14	6	☐	6	☐	12

Strand: Number **Strand Unit:** Counting and numeration; Operations – addition.

5 Add and match

Colour each matching sum and answer the same colour. Match them.

3 + 2		10
5 + 1		6
4 + 3		14
10 + 4		5
12 + 1		7
8 + 2		12
9 + 3		13
0 + 4		3
1 + 2		4
6 + 3		15
11 + 4		9

6 Doubles

(a) 1 and 1 =

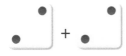

(b) 2 plus 2 =

(c) 3 + 3 =

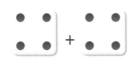

(d) 4 and 4 =

7 Sums with brackets

(a) (4 + 4) + 2 =

(b) (8 + 1) + 3 =

(c) (6 + 3) + 4 =

(d) (9 + 2) + 1 =

(e) (11 + 2) + 1 =

(f) (12 + 4) + 3 =

(g) (1 + 0) + 2 =

8 Problem-solving with tables

Colour the sum that matches each problem.

(a) Tom had **10** stickers. His teacher gave him **2** more. How many stickers does Tom have now?

| 10 − 2 = 8 | or | 10 + 2 = 12 |

(b) Shane had **no** colouring pencils. His friend gave him **4** colouring pencils. How many colouring pencils does Shane have now?

| 0 + 4 = 4 | or | 4 − 4 = 0 |

(c) There were **6** friends at Harry's party. **3** more friends arrived. How many friends are at Harry's party now?

| 3 + 3 = 6 | or | 6 + 3 = 9 |

Rough work

Strand: Number Strand Unit: Counting and numeration; Operations – addition Skill: Problem-solving.

altogether • add • plus • addition • sum of

9 Picture sums

Find the answers to the sums. Colour the picture according to the colour key.

Colour key

10 11 12 13 14

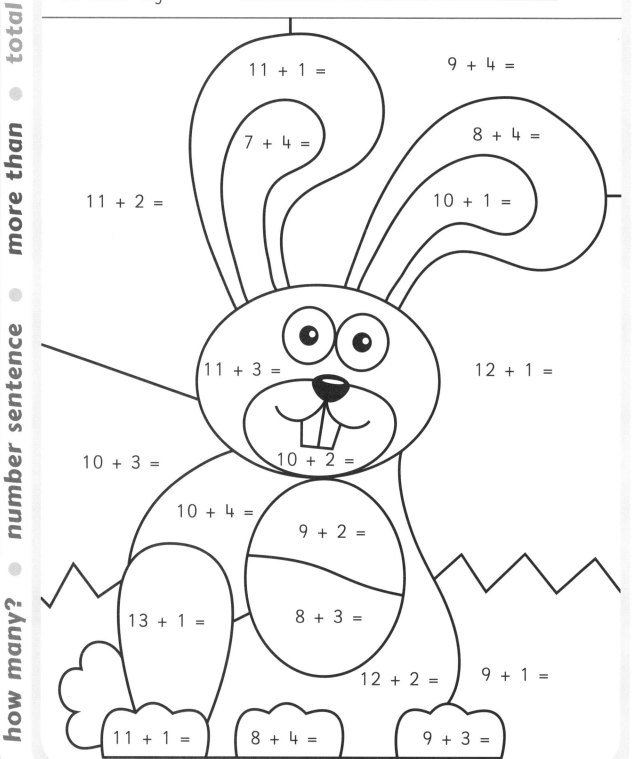

11 + 1 =

9 + 4 =

7 + 4 =

8 + 4 =

11 + 2 =

10 + 1 =

11 + 3 =

12 + 1 =

10 + 3 =

10 + 2 =

10 + 4 =

9 + 2 =

13 + 1 =

8 + 3 =

12 + 2 =

9 + 1 =

11 + 1 =

8 + 4 =

9 + 3 =

sum of • addition • plus • add • and

how many? • number sentence • count on • add on • add up

How did you do? 😊⚪ 😐⚪ 🙁⚪   **Do Test A on page 100.**

Strand: Number **Strand Unit:** Counting and numeration; Operations – addition.

Add 5

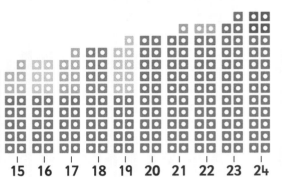

| 0 | 1 | 2 | 3 | 4 | 5 | 6 | 7 | 8 | 9 | 10 | 11 | 12 | 13 | 14 | 15 | 16 | 17 | 18 | 19 | 20 | 21 | 22 | 23 | 24 |

Monday

+ 5 Tables

Monday	0 + 5 = 5
	1 + 5 = 6
	2 + 5 = 7
	3 + 5 = 8
	4 + 5 = 9
	5 + 5 = 10
Tuesday	6 + 5 = 11
	7 + 5 = 12
	8 + 5 = 13
Wednesday	9 + 5 = 14
	10 + 5 = 15
	11 + 5 = 16
	12 + 5 = 17

Look

Say

Cover

Write

Check

Learn these

0 + 5 = 5
1 + 5 = 6
2 + 5 = 7
3 + 5 = 8
4 + 5 = 9

You try!

0 + 5 =
1 + 5 =
2 + 5 =
3 + 5 =
4 + 5 =

1 Add up

 + 5

(a) 2 + 5 =

 + 5

(b) 1 and 5 =

 + 5

(c) 4 + 5 =

 + 5

(d) 3 and 5 =

2 Colour the correct sum

(a)   **+**

| 3 + 4 = 7 | or | 5 − 3 = 2 | or | 3 + 5 = 8 |

(b)   **+**

| 1 + 5 = 6 | or | 1 + 4 = 5 | or | 1 + 6 = 7 |

3 Correct these. ✓ or ✗

 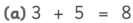

(a) 3 + 5 = 8

(b) 1 + 5 = 7

(c) 2 + 5 = 7

(d) 4 + 5 = 9

(e) 0 + 5 = 5

Tuesday

Learn these

5 + 5 = 10
6 + 5 = 11
7 + 5 = 12
8 + 5 = 13

You try!

5 + 5 =

6 + 5 =

7 + 5 =

8 + 5 =

1 Addition sums

(a)	3	(b)	5	(c)	8	(d)	6	(e)	1
	+ 5		+ 5		+ 5		+ 5		+ 5

(f)	7	(g)	0	(h)	4	(i)	2	(j)	9
	+ 5		+ 5		+ 5		+ 5		+ 5

2 Count on 5

(a) 5 →

(b) 8 →

(c) 7 →

(d) 6 →

(e) 4 →

3 Add up

(a) What is 8 and 5?

(b) What is 5 and 5?

(c) What is 6 and 5?

(d) What is 7 and 5?

(e) What is 4 and 5?

Wednesday

Learn these

9 + 5 = 14
10 + 5 = 15
11 + 5 = 16
12 + 5 = 17

You try!

9 + 5 =

10 + 5 =

11 + 5 =

12 + 5 =

1 Fill in the missing numbers

(a) 9 +   = 14

(b)   + 5 = 16

(c) 10 +   = 15

(d)   + 5 = 17

2 + or – ?

(a) 9   5 = 14

(b) 11   5 = 6

(c) 12   5 = 7

(d) 10   5 = 15

3 Correct these. ✓ or ✗

(a) 12 + 5 = 17

(b) 10 + 5 = 15

(c) 9 + 5 = 14

(d) 11 + 5 = 16

4 Adding money

How much altogether?

c

Strand: Number Strand Unit: Counting and numeration; Operations – addition
Strand: Measures Strand Unit: Money.

Thursday — Revision and Problem-solving

Learn these

0 + 5 =	5
1 + 5 =	6
2 + 5 =	7
3 + 5 =	8
4 + 5 =	9
5 + 5 =	10
6 + 5 =	11
7 + 5 =	12
8 + 5 =	13
9 + 5 =	14
10 + 5 =	15
11 + 5 =	16
12 + 5 =	17

1 Problem-solving with tables

Colour each matching problem and sum the same colour. Write the answer.

Don't forget your... RUCSAC!

(a) Jason has **3** dogs. Anna has **5** dogs. How many dogs do Jason and Anna have altogether?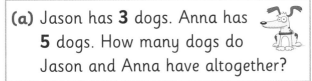

(b) Paul has **8** cent. His mam gives him **5** cent more. How much money does Paul have now?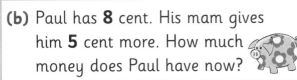

(c) Jim bought **5** oranges and **5** apples. How many pieces of fruit does he have altogether?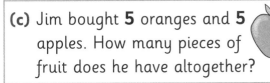

(d) In Claire's class there are **12** girls and **5** boys. How many children are in Claire's class altogether?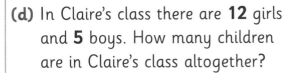

5 + 5 =

8 + 5 =

12 + 5 =

3 + 5 =

2 Colour 'yes' or 'no'

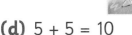

(a) 3 + 5 = 8

yes | no

(b) 1 + 5 = 7

yes | no

(c) 7 + 5 = 12

yes | no

(d) 5 + 5 = 10

yes | no

3 Ring the words that tell us to add

add | and | plus | minus | all

altogether | total | subtract | sum of

Rough work

4 Test yourself!

2 + 5 =	8 + 5 =	10 + 5 =
12 + 5 =	1 + 5 =	5 + 5 =
3 + 5 =	7 + 5 =	6 + 5 =
9 + 5 =	11 + 5 =	
0 + 5 =	4 + 5 =	

My score _____ / 13

How did you do?

Strand: Number Strand Unit: Counting and numeration; Operations – addition
Strand: Measures Strand Unit: Money Skill: Problem-solving.

Do Test 5 on page 95. 21

Add 6

| 0 | 1 | 2 | 3 | 4 | 5 | 6 | 7 | 8 | 9 | 10 | 11 | 12 | 13 | 14 | 15 | 16 | 17 | 18 | 19 | 20 | 21 | 22 | 23 | 24 |

Monday

+ 6 Tables

Monday

0 + 6 = 6
1 + 6 = 7
2 + 6 = 8
3 + 6 = 9
4 + 6 = 10
5 + 6 = 11

Tuesday

6 + 6 = 12
7 + 6 = 13
8 + 6 = 14

Wednesday

9 + 6 = 15
10 + 6 = 16
11 + 6 = 17
12 + 6 = 18

Look

Say

Cover

Write

Check

Learn these

0 + 6 = 6
1 + 6 = 7
2 + 6 = 8
3 + 6 = 9
4 + 6 = 10

You try!

0 + 6 =

1 + 6 =

2 + 6 =

3 + 6 =

4 + 6 =

1 Add 6

Match each number with the correct answer.

+ 6

3	13
7	6
10	9
12	18
0	16
6	8
9	12
2	15
11	17

2 Problem-solving with tables – pet shop

Below are the animals in a pet shop. Answer the questions that follow.

(a) How many cats and goldfish?   1 + 6 = 7

(b) How many dogs and goldfish?

(c) How many frogs and goldfish?

(d) How many goldfish and cats and dogs?

(e) How many frogs and goldfish and rabbits?

Don't forget your...

RUCSAC!

Strand: Number **Strand Unit:** Counting and numeration; Operations – addition **Skill:** Problem-solving.

Tuesday

Learn these

5 + 6 = 11
6 + 6 = 12
7 + 6 = 13
8 + 6 = 14

You try!

5 + 6 =
6 + 6 =
7 + 6 =
8 + 6 =

1 Ring the correct answer

(a) 6 + 6 = 0 or 12   **(b)** 5 + 6 = 10 or 11

(c) 8 + 6 = 14 or 15   **(d)** 7 + 6 = 14 or 13

2 Count on 6

(a) 5 → 11   **(b)** 7 →   **(c)** 3 →

(d) 4 →   **(e)** 8 →   **(f)** 6 →

(g) 0 →   **(h)** 2 →

3 Finish the number sentences

(a) 1 + 6 =   **(b)** 2 + 6 =   **(c)** 7 + 6 =

(d) 5 + 6 =   **(e)** 3 + 6 =   **(f)** 9 + 6 =

(g) 4 + 6 =   **(h)** 8 + 6 =   **(i)** 6 + 6 =

Wednesday

Learn these

9 + 6 = 15
10 + 6 = 16
11 + 6 = 17
12 + 6 = 18

You try!

9 + 6 =
10 + 6 =
11 + 6 =
12 + 6 =

1 Add up

(a) 4 + 6 =

(b) 6 + 3 =

2 Colour ✓ or ✗

(a) 9 + 6 = 15   ✓ ✗

(b) 10 + 6 = 18   ✓ ✗

(c) 12 + 6 = 18   ✓ ✗

(d) 11 + 6 = 17   ✓ ✗

(e) 7 + 6 = 15   ✓ ✗

3 Sums with brackets

(a) (6 + 6) + 2 =

(b) (9 + 6) + 2 =

(c) (11 + 6) + 0 =

(d) (12 + 6) + 3 =

Thursday Revision and Problem-solving

Learn these

0 + 6 = 6
1 + 6 = 7
2 + 6 = 8
3 + 6 = 9
4 + 6 = 10
5 + 6 = 11
6 + 6 = 12
7 + 6 = 13
8 + 6 = 14
9 + 6 = 15
10 + 6 = 16
11 + 6 = 17
12 + 6 = 18

1 Colour the correct sum

(a)  **+**

| 2 + 4 = 6 | or | 2 + 6 = 8 | or | 2 + 5 = 7 |

(b) 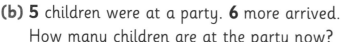 **+**

| 8 + 8 = 16 | or | 6 + 6 = 12 | or | 6 + 0 = 6 |

2 + or – word?

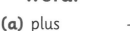

(a) plus   +
(b) add
(c) subtract
(d) altogether
(e) take away
(f) all
(g) minus

Rough work

3 Problem-solving with tables

Write a number sentence to match each problem.

RUCSAC!

(a) An orange costs **10** cent. A lollipop costs **6** cent. How much do they cost altogether?	10 + 6 = 16
(b) **5** children were at a party. **6** more arrived. How many children are at the party now?	
(c) A farmer has **11** pigs and **6** cows. How many animals does he have in total?	
(d) Alan had **4** goldfish. He bought **6** more. How many goldfish does he have now?	

4 Test yourself!

2 + 6 =	8 + 6 =	10 + 6 =
12 + 6 =	1 + 6 =	5 + 6 =
3 + 6 =	7 + 6 =	6 + 6 =
9 + 6 =	11 + 6 =	
0 + 6 =	4 + 6 =	

How did you do?

My score   / 13

Strand: Number **Strand Unit:** Counting and numeration; Operations – addition
Strand: Measures **Strand Unit:** Money **Skill:** Problem-solving.

Do Test 6 on page 95.

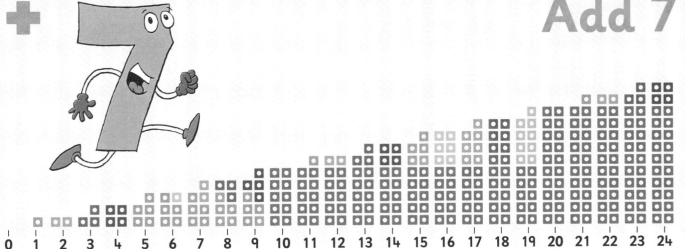

Add 7

0 1 2 3 4 5 6 7 8 9 10 11 12 13 14 15 16 17 18 19 20 21 22 23 24

Monday

+7 Tables

Monday

0	+ 7 =	7
1	+ 7 =	8
2	+ 7 =	9
3	+ 7 =	10
4	+ 7 =	11

Tuesday

5	+ 7 =	12
6	+ 7 =	13
7	+ 7 =	14
8	+ 7 =	15

Wednesday

9	+ 7 =	16
10	+ 7 =	17
11	+ 7 =	18
12	+ 7 =	19

Look

Say

Cover

Write

Check

Learn these

0 + 7 = 7
1 + 7 = 8
2 + 7 = 9
3 + 7 = 10
4 + 7 = 11

You try!

0 + 7 =

1 + 7 =

2 + 7 =

3 + 7 =

4 + 7 =

1 Count on

(a)  + 7 =

(b) + 7 =

(c) 0 + =

(d) + 7 =

(e) 7 + =

2 Adding money

(a)   and

equals [ ] cent

(b) and

makes [ ] cent

(c)   +

= [ ] cent

(d)   +

is the same as [ ] cent

Strand: Number **Strand Unit:** Counting and numeration; Operations – addition
Strand: Measures **Strand Unit:** Money.

Tuesday

Learn these

5 + 7 = 12
6 + 7 = 13
7 + 7 = 14
8 + 7 = 15

You try!

5 + 7 =

6 + 7 =

7 + 7 =

8 + 7 =

1 Addition sums

(a)	(b)	(c)	(d)	(e)
7	5	8	6	1
+ 7	+ 7	+ 7	+ 7	+ 7

(f)	(g)	(h)	(i)	(j)
3	0	10	9	12
+ 7	+ 7	+ 7	+ 7	+ 7

2 Fill in the missing numbers

(a) and 7 frogs = [ ] frogs

(b)  and [ ] flowers = 12 flowers

(c) [ ] pencils and 7 pencils =

Wednesday

Learn these

9 + 7 = 16
10 + 7 = 17
11 + 7 = 18
12 + 7 = 19

You try!

9 + 7 =

10 + 7 =

11 + 7 =

12 + 7 =

1 Fill in the missing numbers

(a) 9 + [ ] = 16

(b) [ ] + 7 = 18

(c) 10 + [ ] = 17

(d) [ ] + 7 = 19

2 + or – ?

(a) 9 [ ] 7 = 16

(b) 11 [ ] 7 = 4

(c) 12 [ ] 7 = 19

(d) 10 [ ] 7 = 3

(e) 8 [ ] 7 = 15

3 Count on 7

(a) 5 →

(b) 8 →

(c) 7 →

(d) 6 →

(e) 10 →

(f) 12 →

4 Correct these. ✓ or ✗

(a) 5 + 7 = 12

(b) 7 + 7 = 14

(c) 8 + 7 = 15

(d) 6 + 7 = 12

(e) 9 + 7 = 16

Strand: Number **Strand Unit:** Counting and numeration; Operations – addition.

Thursday — Revision and Problem-solving

Learn these

0 + 7	=	7
1 + 7	=	8
2 + 7	=	9
3 + 7	=	10
4 + 7	=	11
5 + 7	=	12
6 + 7	=	13
7 + 7	=	14
8 + 7	=	15
9 + 7	=	16
10 + 7	=	17
11 + 7	=	18
12 + 7	=	19

1 Problem-solving with tables

Colour each matching problem and sum the same colour. Write the answer.

Don't forget your... RUCSAC!

(a) Cian has **11** cent. His mam gives him another **7** cent. How much money does Cian have now?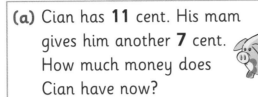

(b) Donal has **9** books. His friend gives him **7** more. How many books does Donal have now?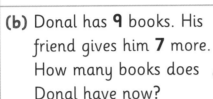

(c) Ciara has **12** sweets. Her nana gives her **7** more. How many sweets does Ciara have now?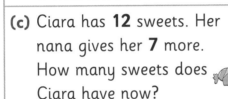

9 + 7 =

12 + 7 =

11 + 7 =

2 Fill in the missing numbers

(a)   and    = _____ ducks

(b) and _____ buns =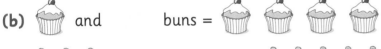

(c) and _____ pencils =

Rough work

3 Test yourself!

2 + 7 =	8 + 7 =	10 + 7 =
12 + 7 =	1 + 7 =	5 + 7 =
3 + 7 =	7 + 7 =	6 + 7 =
9 + 7 =	11 + 7 =	
0 + 7 =	4 + 7 =	

My score _____ / 13

How did you do?

Strand: Number **Strand Unit:** Counting and numeration; Operations – addition
Strand: Measures **Strand Unit:** Money **Skill:** Problem-solving.

Do Test 7 on page 95.

27

Add 8

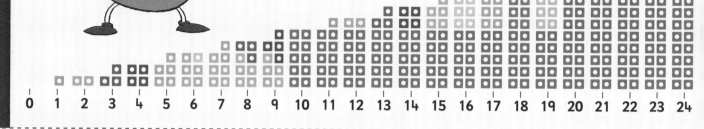

| 0 1 2 3 4 5 6 7 8 9 10 11 12 13 14 15 16 17 18 19 20 21 22 23 24 |

Monday

+ 8 Tables

Monday	0 + 8 =	8
	1 + 8 =	9
	2 + 8 =	10
	3 + 8 =	11
	4 + 8 =	12
Tuesday	5 + 8 =	13
	6 + 8 =	14
	7 + 8 =	15
	8 + 8 =	16
Wednesday	9 + 8 =	17
	10 + 8 =	18
	11 + 8 =	19
	12 + 8 =	20

Look
Say
Cover
Write
Check

Learn these

0 + 8 = 8
1 + 8 = 9
2 + 8 = 10
3 + 8 = 11
4 + 8 = 12

You try!

0 + 8 =
1 + 8 =
2 + 8 =
3 + 8 =
4 + 8 =

1 Add up

(a)  + 8 =

(b) 0 + 8 =

(c) 🦋 + 8 =

(d) 🗝🗝 + 8 =

(e) 💡💡💡💡 + 8 =

2 Fill in the missing numbers

(a) + [ ] = 11

(b) [ ] +  = 10

(c) [ ] +  = 12

3 Plus 8

		+ 8
(a)	1	9
(b)	0	
(c)	4	
(d)	2	
(e)	3	

Strand: Number **Strand Unit:** Counting and numeration; Operations – addition.

Tuesday

Learn these

5 + 8 = 13
6 + 8 = 14
7 + 8 = 15
8 + 8 = 16

You try!

5 + 8 =

6 + 8 =

7 + 8 =

8 + 8 =

1 Finish the number sentences

(a) 5 + 8 =

(b) 8 + 8 =

(c) 3 + 8 =

(d) 0 + 8 =

(e) 7 + 8 =

(f) 2 + 8 =

(g) 4 + 8 =

(h) 1 + 8 =

(i) 12 + 8 =

(j) 10 + 8 =

2 Fill in the missing numbers

(a) 5 + ___ = 13

(b) ___ + 8 = 16

(c) 6 + ___ = 14

(d) ___ + 8 = 15

3 Correct these. ✓ or ✗

(a) 7 + 8 = 15

(b) 0 + 8 = 0

(c) 5 + 8 = 13

(d) 8 + 8 = 16

Wednesday

Learn these

9 + 8 = 17
10 + 8 = 18
11 + 8 = 19
12 + 8 = 20

You try!

9 + 8 =

10 + 8 =

11 + 8 =

12 + 8 =

1 + or – ?

(a) 9 ___ 8 = 17

(b) 11 ___ 8 = 3

(c) 12 ___ 8 = 4

(d) 10 ___ 8 = 18

3 Sums with brackets

(a) (7 + 8) + 2 =

(b) (5 + 8) + 4 =

(c) (11 + 8) + 3 =

(d) (12 + 8) + 4 =

2 Add 8

Match each number with the correct answer.

+ 8

3	15
7	11
10	20
12	8
0	14
6	18
11	17
9	19

Strand: Number **Strand Unit:** Counting and numeration; Operations – addition.

Thursday — Revision and Problem-solving

Learn these

0 + 8 = 8
1 + 8 = 9
2 + 8 = 10
3 + 8 = 11
4 + 8 = 12
5 + 8 = 13
6 + 8 = 14
7 + 8 = 15
8 + 8 = 16
9 + 8 = 17
10 + 8 = 18
11 + 8 = 19
12 + 8 = 20

1 Problem-solving with tables

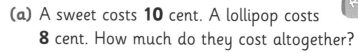

Don't forget your... **RUCSAC!**

Colour the sum that matches each problem.

(a) A sweet costs **10** cent. A lollipop costs **8** cent. How much do they cost altogether?

$$10 - 8 = 2 \quad \text{or} \quad 10 + 8 = 18$$

(b) There are **20** children in Second Class. **8** children go home sick. How many children are still at school?

$$20 + 8 = 28 \quad \text{or} \quad 20 - 8 = 12$$

(c) A florist put **6** flowers in a vase. He put another **8** flowers in the vase. How many flowers are in the vase now?

$$6 + 8 = 14 \quad \text{or} \quad 8 + 6 = 16$$

(d) A pet shop owner had **16** snakes. She sold **half** of them. How many snakes does she have now?

$$16 + 16 = 32 \quad \text{or} \quad 16 - 8 = 8$$

2 Add and draw

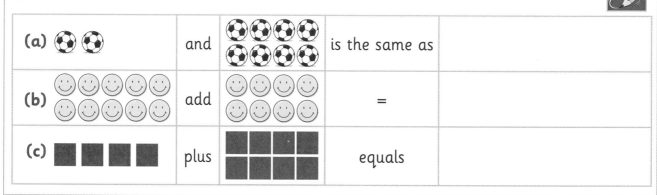

(a) ⚽ ⚽	and	⚽⚽⚽⚽⚽ ⚽⚽⚽⚽⚽	is the same as	
(b) ☺☺☺☺☺ ☺☺☺☺☺	add	☺☺☺☺ ☺☺☺☺	=	
(c) ■ ■ ■ ■	plus	■■■■ ■■■■	equals	

3 Test yourself!

2 + 8 =   8 + 8 =   10 + 8 =

12 + 8 =   1 + 8 =   5 + 8 =

3 + 8 =   7 + 8 =   6 + 8 =

9 + 8 =   11 + 8 =

0 + 8 =   4 + 8 =

How did you do?

My score ☐ / 13

Strand: Number **Strand Unit:** Counting and numeration; Operations – addition
Strand: Measures **Strand Unit:** Money **Skill:** Problem-solving.

Do Test 8 on page 95.

Problem-solving and Revision

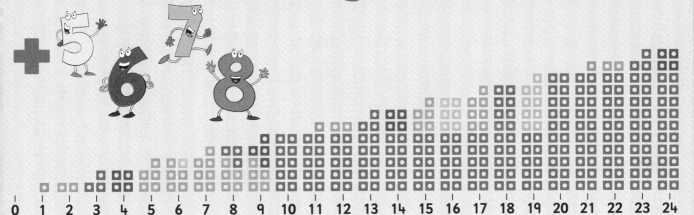

0 1 2 3 4 5 6 7 8 9 10 11 12 13 14 15 16 17 18 19 20 21 22 23 24

---

1 Test your memory!

Finish these number sentences.

(a) 6 + 5 =   (b) 8 + 7 =   (c) 5 + 7 =

(b) 7 + 8 =   (e) 9 + 5 =   (f) 4 + 6 =

(g) 2 + 7 =   (h) 10 + 8 =   (i) 12 + 5 =

(j) 8 + 6 =   (k) 11 + 7 =   (l) 12 + 8 =

(m) 7 + 5 =   (n) 8 + 8 =   (o) 11 + 8 =

(p) 9 + 8 =   (q) 3 + 5 =   (r) 12 + 6 =

---

2 Find the total

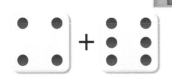

(a) 4 + 6 =

(b) 6 + 6 =

---

3 Crack the code!

Complete the number sentences to crack the code.

1 + 5 =	**c**	8 + 5 =	**d**
9 + 8 =	**e**	9 + 6 =	**k**
2 + 6 =	**o**	2 + 8 =	**r**
12 + 7 =	**b**	4 + 7 =	**n**

6   8   13   17   19   10   8   15   17   11   **!**

---

4 Fill in the missing numbers

(a)   9   (b)   12   (c)   3   (d)   0   (e)   5   (f)   7   (g)   10

    + 5   +   +   + 8   +   + 7   +

   _____   18   10   _____   10   _____   16

Strand: Number Strand Unit: Counting and numeration; Operations – addition.

5 Tricky sums

(a) ___ plus 5 = 7   (b) ___ and 6 is the same as 6

(c) ___ plus 7 = 12   (d) ___ and 8 is the same as 14

(e) ___ plus 8 = 19   (f) ___ and 5 is the same as 15

(g) ___ plus 5 = 5   (h) ___ and 6 is the same as 13

6 Add and match

Colour each matching sum and answer the same colour. Match them.

3 + 6	18
5 + 5	17
4 + 7	11
10 + 8	9
12 + 5	10
9 + 7	7
0 + 8	12
1 + 6	19
6 + 6	8
12 + 7	16

7 What is missing?

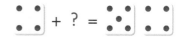

(a) 4 + ___ = 9

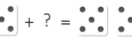

(b) 5 + ___ = 10

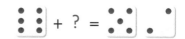

(c) 5 + ___ = 11

(d) 6 + ___ = 7

8 Unscramble the sums

(a)
```
    + 5
2        7
```
2 + 5 = 7

(b)
```
    + 8
17       9
```

(c)
```
    9
+ 6      15
```

9 Problem-solving with tables

Don't forget your...

RUCSAC!

Colour the sum that matches each problem.

(a) Tina's cat weighs **5** kilograms. Donal's dog weighs **8** kilograms. How many kilograms do the two pets weigh altogether?

5 + 8 = 13   or   8 − 5 = 3

(b) Shane ran **3** kilometres. Sheena ran **6** kilometres. How many kilometres did Shane and Sheena run between them?

6 − 3 = 3   or   3 + 6 = 9

(c) There were **6** friends at Harry's party. **8** more friends arrived. A little later, **4** friends arrived. How many friends are at Harry's party now?

6 + 8 = 14   or   6 + 8 + 4 = 18

Rough work

Strand: Number **Strand Unit:** Counting and numeration; Operations – addition
Strand: Measures **Strand Unit:** Weight, Length **Skill:** Problem-solving.

10 Picture sums

Find the answers to the sums. Colour the picture according to the colour key.

Colour key

11 12 13 14

6 + 6 =

4 + 8 =

8 + 5 =

7 + 6 =

6 + 8 =

8 + 6 =

6 + 7 =

7 + 7 =

9 + 5 =

7 + 5 =

5 + 8 =

3 + 8 =

How did you do?   **Do Test B on page 100.**

Strand: Number Strand Unit: Counting and numeration; Operations – addition.

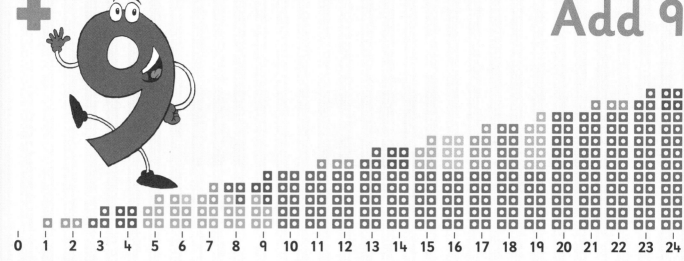

Add 9

0 1 2 3 4 5 6 7 8 9 10 11 12 13 14 15 16 17 18 19 20 21 22 23 24

Monday

+ 9 Tables

Monday
- 0 + 9 = 9
- 1 + 9 = 10
- 2 + 9 = 11
- 3 + 9 = 12
- 4 + 9 = 13

Tuesday
- 5 + 9 = 14
- 6 + 9 = 15
- 7 + 9 = 16
- 8 + 9 = 17

Wednesday
- 9 + 9 = 18
- 10 + 9 = 19
- 11 + 9 = 20
- 12 + 9 = 21

Look

Say

Cover

Write

Check

Learn these

- 0 + 9 = 9
- 1 + 9 = 10
- 2 + 9 = 11
- 3 + 9 = 12
- 4 + 9 = 13

You try!

- 0 + 9 =
- 1 + 9 =
- 2 + 9 =
- 3 + 9 =
- 4 + 9 =

1 Count on

 + 9

(a) What is 2 + 9?

 + 9

(b) 1 and 9 =

 + 9

(c) What is 4 + 9?

 + 9

(d) 3 and 9 =

2 Colour the correct sum

(a)

3 + 9 = 12	or	12 + 0 = 12	or	3 + 8 = 11

(b)

1 + 10 = 11	or	10 – 9 = 1	or	1 + 9 = 10

3 Correct these. ✓ or ✗

(a) 3 + 9 = 12

(b) 1 + 9 = 10

(c) 2 + 9 = 11

(d) 4 + 9 = 14

(e) 0 + 9 = 9

Strand: Number **Strand Unit:** Counting and numeration; Operations – addition.

Tuesday

Learn these

5 + 9 = 14
6 + 9 = 15
7 + 9 = 16
8 + 9 = 17

You try!

5 + 9 =

6 + 9 =

7 + 9 =

8 + 9 =

1 Addition sums

(a)   3   (b)   5   (c)   8   (d)   6   (e)   1
      + 9   + 9   + 9   + 9   + 9

(f)   7   (g)   0   (h)   4   (i)   2   (j)   9
      + 9   + 9   + 9   + 9   + 9

2 Count on 9

(a) 5 →

(b) 8 →

(c) 7 →

(d) 6 →

(e) 4 →

3 Add up

(a) What is 8 plus 9?

(b) What is 5 plus 9?

(c) What is 6 plus 9?

(d) What is 7 plus 9?

(e) What is 3 plus 9?

Wednesday

Learn these

9 + 9 = 18
10 + 9 = 19
11 + 9 = 20
12 + 9 = 21

You try!

9 + 9 =

10 + 9 =

11 + 9 =

12 + 9 =

1 Fill in the missing numbers

(a) 9 +   = 18

(b)   + 9 = 21

(c) 10 +   = 19

(d)   + 9 = 20

2 + or – ?

(a) 9   9 = 18

(b) 11   9 = 2

(c) 12   9 = 21

(d) 10   9 = 19

(e) 8   9 = 17

3 Correct these. ✓ or ✗

(a) 12 + 9 = 19

(b) 10 + 9 = 19

(c) 9 + 9 = 18

(d) 11 + 9 = 2

4 Adding money

How much altogether?

c

Strand: Number Strand Unit: Counting and numeration; Operations – addition
Strand: Measures Strand Unit: Money.

Thursday — Revision and Problem-solving

Learn these

$0 + 9 = 9$
$1 + 9 = 10$
$2 + 9 = 11$
$3 + 9 = 12$
$4 + 9 = 13$
$5 + 9 = 14$
$6 + 9 = 15$
$7 + 9 = 16$
$8 + 9 = 17$
$9 + 9 = 18$
$10 + 9 = 19$
$11 + 9 = 20$
$12 + 9 = 21$

1 Problem-solving with tables

Colour each matching problem and sum the same colour. Write the answer.

(a) Amy's dog has **6** puppies. Lisa's dog has **9** puppies. How many puppies do they have altogether?

(b) Tina had **12** cent. Her sister gave her **9** cent more. How much money did Tina have then?

(c) Liz ran **10** kilometres. Then she cycled **9** kilometres. How far did she travel altogether?

(d) In Danny's class there are **11** girls and **9** boys. How many children are in Danny's class altogether?

$11 + 9 =$

$6 + 9 =$

$10 + 9 =$

$12 + 9 =$

Don't forget your... RUCSAC!

2 Colour 'yes' or 'no'

(a) $3 + 9 = 12$ yes   no

(b) $1 + 9 = 10$ yes   no

(c) $7 + 9 = 16$ yes   no

(d) $5 + 9 = 4$ yes   no

3 Ring the words that tell us to add

| minus | plus | add | subtract |

| less than | total | greater than |

Rough work

4 Test yourself!

$2 + 9 =$ $8 + 9 =$ $10 + 9 =$

$12 + 9 =$ $1 + 9 =$ $5 + 9 =$

$3 + 9 =$ $7 + 9 =$ $6 + 9 =$

$9 + 9 =$ $11 + 9 =$

$0 + 9 =$ $4 + 9 =$

My score ☐ / 13

How did you do?

☺ ○
😐 ○
☹ ○

Strand: Number **Strand Unit:** Counting and numeration; Operations – addition
Strand: Measures **Strand Unit:** Money, Length **Skill:** Problem-solving.

Do Test 9 on page 96.

0 1 2 3 4 5 6 7 8 9 10 11 12 13 14 15 16 17 18 19 20 21 22 23 24

Monday

+ 10 Tables

Monday	0 + 10 = 10
	1 + 10 = 11
	2 + 10 = 12
	3 + 10 = 13
	4 + 10 = 14
	5 + 10 = 15
Tuesday	6 + 10 = 16
	7 + 10 = 17
	8 + 10 = 18
	9 + 10 = 19
Wednesday	10 + 10 = 20
	11 + 10 = 21
	12 + 10 = 22

Look

Say

Cover

Write

Check

Learn these

0 + 10 = 10
1 + 10 = 11
2 + 10 = 12
3 + 10 = 13
4 + 10 = 14

You try!

0 + 10 =

1 + 10 =

2 + 10 =

3 + 10 =

4 + 10 =

1 Add 10

Match each number with the correct answer.

+ 10

3	10
7	22
10	13
12	17
0	21
6	16
9	12
2	20
11	19

2 Problem-solving with tables – sweet shop

Don't forget your... RUCSAC!

Below are the prices of sweets in a sweet shop. Answer the questions that follow.

 10c   22c   18c    10c

(a) How much do a candy cane and a sweet cost?   22 + 10 = 32

(b) How much do a candy cane and a lollipop cost?

(c) How much do a lollipop and a sweet cost?

(d) How much do a bun and a lollipop cost?

(e) How much do **two** lollipops and a sweet cost **altogether?**

Strand: Number **Strand Unit:** Counting and numeration; Operations – addition
Strand: Measures **Strand Unit:** Money **Skill:** Problem-solving.

Tuesday

Learn these

5 + 10 = 15
6 + 10 = 16
7 + 10 = 17
8 + 10 = 18

You try!

5 + 10 =

6 + 10 =

7 + 10 =

8 + 10 =

1 Ring the correct answer

(a) 6 + 10 = 16 or 26

(b) 5 + 10 = 5 or 15

(c) 8 + 10 = 18 or 19

(d) 7 + 10 = 7 or 17

2 Count on 10

(a) 5 → 15   (b) 7 →

(c) 3 →   (d) 4 →

(e) 8 →   (f) 6 →

(g) 0 →   (h) 2 →

3 Finish the number sentences

(a) 1 + 10 =   (b) 2 + 10 =

(c) 7 + 10 =   (d) 5 + 10 =

(e) 3 + 10 =   (f) 9 + 10 =

(g) 4 + 10 =   (h) 8 + 10 =

(i) 6 + 10 =   (j) 10 + 10 =

Wednesday

Learn these

9 + 10 = 19
10 + 10 = 20
11 + 10 = 21
12 + 10 = 22

You try!

9 + 10 =

10 + 10 =

11 + 10 =

12 + 10 =

1 Add up

(a) 3 + 10 =

(b) 2 + 10 =

2 Colour ✓ or ✗

(a) 9 + 10 = 19 ✓ ✗

(b) 10 + 10 = 30 ✓ ✗

(c) 12 + 10 = 22 ✓ ✗

(d) 11 + 10 = 21 ✓ ✗

(e) 5 + 10 = 25 ✓ ✗

3 Sums with brackets

(a) (6 + 10) + 6 =

(b) (9 + 10) + 5 =

(c) (11 + 10) + 0 =

(d) (12 + 10) + 3 =

Strand: Number Strand Unit: Counting and numeration; Operations – addition.

Thursday   Revision and Problem-solving

Learn these

0 + 10	= 10
1 + 10	= 11
2 + 10	= 12
3 + 10	= 13
4 + 10	= 14
5 + 10	= 15
6 + 10	= 16
7 + 10	= 17
8 + 10	= 18
9 + 10	= 19
10 + 10	= 20
11 + 10	= 21
12 + 10	= 22

1 Colour the correct sum

(a)

2 + 10 = 12	or	2 + 11 = 13

or | 2 + 6 = 8 |

(b)

6 + 6 = 12	or	6 + 10 = 16

or | 6 + 8 = 14 |

2 + or – word?

(a) plus   +

(b) add

(c) subtract

(d) altogether

(e) take away

(f) all

(g) minus

3 Problem-solving with tables

Write a number sentence to match each problem.

(a) A bar costs **12** cent. A lollipop costs **10** cent. How much do they cost altogether?	
(b) There were **24** cows in a field. **10** cows got out! How many cows are in the field now?	
(c) James read **12** books. Lisa read **10** books. How many books did they read in total?	

Rough work

4 Test yourself!

2 + 10 =	8 + 10 =	10 + 10 =
12 + 10 =	1 + 10 =	5 + 10 =
3 + 10 =	7 + 10 =	6 + 10 =
9 + 10 =	11 + 10 =	
0 + 10 =	4 + 10 =	

My score [   ] / 13

How did you do?

Strand: Number Strand Unit: Counting and numeration; Operations – addition
Strand: Measures Strand Unit: Money Skill: Problem-solving.

Do Test 10 on page 96.

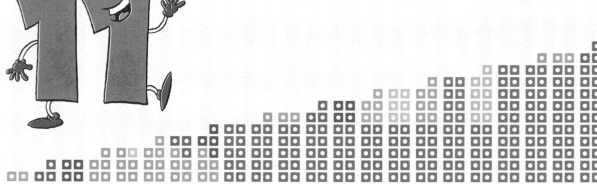

Add 11

Monday

+ 11 Tables

Monday	0 + 11 = 11
	1 + 11 = 12
	2 + 11 = 13
	3 + 11 = 14
	4 + 11 = 15
Tuesday	5 + 11 = 16
	6 + 11 = 17
	7 + 11 = 18
	8 + 11 = 19
	9 + 11 = 20
Wednesday	10 + 11 = 21
	11 + 11 = 22
	12 + 11 = 23

Look

Say

Cover

Write

Check

Learn these

0 + 11 = 11

1 + 11 = 12

2 + 11 = 13

3 + 11 = 14

4 + 11 = 15

You try!

0 + 11 =

1 + 11 =

2 + 11 =

3 + 11 =

4 + 11 =

1 Count on

(a) 🚗 🚗 + 11 =

(b) 🐴 + 11 =

(c) 0 + 🍃🍃🍃🍃🍃🍃 =

(d) + 11 =

(e) 11 + =

2 Adding money

(a) and

equals ____ cent

(b) +

makes ____ cent

(c) and

= ____ cent

(d)   +

is the same as ____ cent

Strand: Number **Strand Unit:** Counting and numeration; Operations – addition
Strand: Measures **Strand Unit:** Money.

Tuesday

Learn these

5 + 11 = 16
6 + 11 = 17
7 + 11 = 18
8 + 11 = 19

You try!

5 + 11 =

6 + 11 =

7 + 11 =

8 + 11 =

1 Addition sums

(a)   7   (b)   5   (c)   8   (d)   6   (e)   1
    + 11   + 11   + 11   + 11   + 11

(f)   3   (g)   0   (h)   10   (i)   11   (j)   12
    + 11   + 11   + 11   + 11   + 11

2 Fill in the missing numbers

(a) and 11 frogs = _____ frogs

(b) and _____ flowers = 16 flowers

(c) and 11 pencils = _____ pencils

Wednesday

Learn these

 9 + 11 = 20
10 + 11 = 21
11 + 11 = 22
12 + 11 = 23

You try!

9 + 11 =

10 + 11 =

11 + 11 =

12 + 11 =

1 Fill in the missing numbers

(a) 9 + _____ = 20

(b) _____ + 11 = 22

(c) 10 + _____ = 21

(d) _____ + 11 = 23

2 + or – ?

(a) 9 ___ 11 = 20

(b) 11 ___ 11 = 0

(c) 12 ___ 11 = 23

(d) 10 ___ 11 = 21

(e) 8 ___ 11 = 19

3 Count on 11

(a) 5 →

(b) 8 →

(c) 7 →

(d) 6 →

(e) 9 →

(f) 11 →

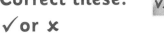

4 Correct these. ✓ or ✗

(a) 5 + 11 = 17

(b) 7 + 11 = 18

(c) 8 + 11 = 19

(d) 6 + 11 = 15

(e) 9 + 11 = 19

Strand: Number **Strand Unit:** Counting and numeration; Operations – addition.

Thursday Revision and Problem-solving

Learn these

0 + 11	=	11
1 + 11	=	12
2 + 11	=	13
3 + 11	=	14
4 + 11	=	15
5 + 11	=	16
6 + 11	=	17
7 + 11	=	18
8 + 11	=	19
9 + 11	=	20
10 + 11	=	21
11 + 11	=	22
12 + 11	=	23

1 Problem-solving with tables

Colour each matching problem and sum the same colour. Write the answer.

Don't forget your... RUCSAC!

(a) Kevin had **10** stamps. His uncle gave him another **11** stamps. How many stamps does Kevin have now?

(b) Donna had **11** pencils. Then her friend gave her the same amount of pencils again. How many pencils does Donna have now?

(c) A farmer had **50** sheep. She sold **11** sheep. How many sheep does she have now?

11 + 11 =

50 − 11 =

10 + 11 =

2 Add and draw

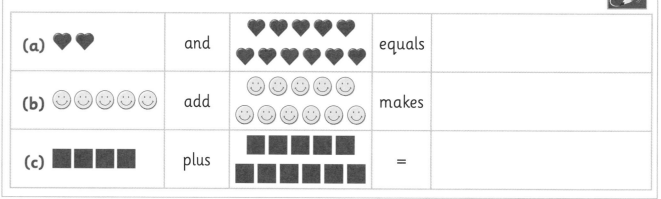

(a) ♥♥	and	♥♥♥♥♥ ♥♥♥♥♥	equals	
(b) ☺☺☺☺☺	add	☺☺☺☺☺ ☺☺☺☺☺	makes	
(c) ▪▪▪▪	plus	▪▪▪▪▪ ▪▪▪▪▪▪	=	

Rough work

3 Test yourself!

2 + 11 =	8 + 11 =	10 + 11 =
12 + 11 =	1 + 11 =	5 + 11 =
3 + 11 =	7 + 11 =	6 + 11 =
9 + 11 =	11 + 11 =	
0 + 11 =	4 + 11 =	

How did you do?

☺ ○
😐 ○
☹ ○

My score ___ / 13

Strand: Number Strand Unit: Counting and numeration; Operations – addition Skill: Problem-solving.

Do Test 11 on page 96.

Add 12

0 1 2 3 4 5 6 7 8 9 10 11 12 13 14 15 16 17 18 19 20 21 22 23 24

Monday

+ 12 Tables

Monday	0 + 12 = 12
	1 + 12 = 13
	2 + 12 = 14
	3 + 12 = 15
	4 + 12 = 16
	5 + 12 = 17
Tuesday	6 + 12 = 18
	7 + 12 = 19
	8 + 12 = 20
	9 + 12 = 21
Wednesday	10 + 12 = 22
	11 + 12 = 23
	12 + 12 = 24

Look

Say

Cover

Write

Check

Learn these

0 + 12 = 12
1 + 12 = 13
2 + 12 = 14
3 + 12 = 15
4 + 12 = 16

You try!

0 + 12 =
1 + 12 =
2 + 12 =
3 + 12 =
4 + 12 =

1 Count on

(a) + 12 =

(b) 0 + 12 =

(c) + 12 =

(d)  + 12 =

(e)  + 12 =

2 Fill in the missing numbers

(a)  + ___ = 15

(b) ___ +  = 20

(c)  + 12 =

3 Plus 12

+ 12

(a) 1   13
(b) 0
(c) 4
(d) 2
(e) 3

Tuesday

Learn these

5 + 12 = 17
6 + 12 = 18
7 + 12 = 19
8 + 12 = 20

You try!

5 + 12 =

6 + 12 =

7 + 12 =

8 + 12 =

1 Finish the number sentences

(a) 5 + 12 =

(b) 8 + 12 =

(c) 3 + 12 =

(d) 0 + 12 =

(e) 7 + 12 =

(f) 2 + 12 =

(g) 4 + 12 =

(h) 1 + 12 =

(i) 12 + 12 =

(j) 10 + 12 =

2 Fill in the missing numbers

(a) 5 +   = 17

(b)   + 12 = 20

(c) 6 +   = 18

(d)   + 12 = 19

3 Correct these. ✓ or ✗

(a) 7 + 12 = 19

(b) 0 + 12 = 0

(c) 5 + 12 = 17

(d) 8 + 12 = 20

Wednesday

Learn these

9 + 12 = 21
10 + 12 = 22
11 + 12 = 23
12 + 12 = 24

You try!

9 + 12 =

10 + 12 =

11 + 12 =

12 + 12 =

1 + or – ?

(a) 9   12 = 21

(b) 11   12 = 23

(c) 12   12 = 0

(d) 10   12 = 22

(e) 24   12 = 12

3 Sums with brackets

(a) (7 + 12) + 2 =

(b) (5 + 12) + 5 =

(c) (11 + 12) + 3 =

(d) (12 + 12) + 0 =

2 Add 12

Match each number with the correct answer.

+ 12

3	19
7	15
10	24
12	12
0	18
6	21
11	23
9	22

Strand: Number **Strand Unit:** Counting and numeration; Operations – addition.

Thursday — Revision and Problem-solving

Learn these

$$0 + 12 = 12$$
$$1 + 12 = 13$$
$$2 + 12 = 14$$
$$3 + 12 = 15$$
$$4 + 12 = 16$$
$$5 + 12 = 17$$
$$6 + 12 = 18$$
$$7 + 12 = 19$$
$$8 + 12 = 20$$
$$9 + 12 = 21$$
$$10 + 12 = 22$$
$$11 + 12 = 23$$
$$12 + 12 = 24$$

1 Problem-solving with tables

Colour the sum that matches each problem.

(a) There are **24** children in John's class. Half of the children went home sick. How many children are still at school?

| $24 + 12 = 36$ | or | $24 - 12 = 12$ |

(b) Kate has **5** marbles. May has **12** marbles **more** than Kate. How many marbles do the girls have in total?

| $5 + 12 = 17$ | or | $5 + 17 = 22$ |

(c) Jill ran **5** kilometres, walked **7** kilometres and cycled **12** kilometres. How far did she travel in total?

| $5 + 7 = 12$ | or | $5 + 7 + 12 = 24$ |

(d) A ruler costs **8** cent. A copybook costs **12** cent **more** than a ruler. How much do the two items cost altogether?

| $8 + 20 = 28$ | or | $8 + 12 = 20$ |

2 Add and draw

| (a) ⚽⚽ and | ⚽⚽⚽⚽⚽⚽ ⚽⚽⚽⚽⚽⚽ | is the same as | |
| (b) ☺ add | ☺☺☺☺☺☺ ☺☺☺☺☺☺ | = | |

Rough work

3 Test yourself!

$2 + 12 =$ $8 + 12 =$ $10 + 12 =$

$12 + 12 =$ $1 + 12 =$ $5 + 12 =$

$3 + 12 =$ $7 + 12 =$ $6 + 12 =$

$9 + 12 =$ $11 + 12 =$

$0 + 12 =$ $4 + 12 =$

How did you do?

My score / 13

Strand: Number **Strand Unit:** Counting and numeration; Operations – addition
Strand: Measures **Strand Units:** Length, Money **Skill:** Problem-solving.

Do Test 12 on page 96.

45

Revision and Problem-solving

0 1 2 3 4 5 6 7 8 9 10 11 12 13 14 15 16 17 18 19 20 21 22 23 24

1 **Test your memory!**

Finish these number sentences.

(a) 6 + 9 =   (b) 8 + 10 =   (c) 5 + 11 =

(d) 7 + 12 =   (e) 9 + 9 =   (f) 4 + 10 =

(g) 2 + 11 =   (h) 10 + 12 =   (i) 12 + 9 =

(j) 8 + 10 =   (k) 11 + 11 =   (l) 12 + 12 =

(m) 7 + 9 =   (n) 8 + 12 =   (o) 11 + 12 =

(p) 9 + 12 =   (q) 3 + 9 =   (r) 12 + 10 =

2 **Find the total**

(a) 4 + 10 =

(b) 6 + 12 =

3 **Crack the code!**

Complete the number sentences to crack the code.

10 + 12 =   **t**   2 + 10 =   **a**

8 + 10 =   **l**   2 + 9 =   **r**

9 + 11 =   **e**   12 + 9 =   **b**

11 + 12 =   **s**

22   12   21   18   20   23   23   22   12   11

4 **Fill in the missing numbers**

(a)   9   (b)   12   (c)   3   (d)   0   (e)   5   (f)   7   (g)   10
  + 9   +   +   + 12   +   + 11   +
  _____   _____   _____   _____   _____   _____   _____
              22   14   14   22

Strand: Number **Strand Unit:** Counting and numeration; Operations – addition.

5 Tricky sums

(a) ____ plus 12 = 17   (b) ____ + 10 = 14

(c) ____ plus 12 = 12   (d) ____ and 9 = 18

(e) ____ + 9 = 15   (f) ____ plus 10 = 19

(g) ____ plus 11 = 12   (h) ____ + 11 = 23

6 Add and match

Colour each matching sum and answer the same colour. Match them.

3 + 9	14
5 + 11	16
4 + 10	19
10 + 9	12
12 + 12	18
8 + 10	24
9 + 11	20
0 + 9	13
1 + 12	23
6 + 9	9
12 + 11	15

7 What is missing?

 + ? = [dominoes]

(a) 2 + ____ = 12

[domino] + ? = [dominoes]

(b) 1 + ____ = 11

[domino] + ? = [dominoes]

(c) 1 + ____ = 10

[domino] + ? = [dominoes]

(d) 4 + ____ = 9

8 Sums with brackets

(a) (4 + 9) + 2 = ____

(b) (8 + 10) + 3 = ____

(c) (6 + 11) + 4 = ____

(d) (9 + 12) + 1 = ____

(e) (11 + 9) + 1 = ____

(f) (12 + 10) + 3 = ____

(g) (1 + 11) + 2 = ____

Rough work

9 Problem-solving with tables

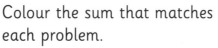

Colour the sum that matches each problem.

(a) Tessa cycled **9** kilometres. Amy cycled **11** kilometres. How many kilometres did the girls cycle altogether?

9 + 11 = 20   or   11 – 9 = 2

(b) Jim's hamster weighs **1** kilogram. Gemma's dog weighs **9** kilograms. How many kilograms do the two pets weigh altogether?

1 + 9 = 10   or   9 – 1 = 8

(c) Bobby read **7** pages of his favourite book on Monday. He read **6** pages on Tuesday and **9** pages on Wednesday. How many pages did Bobby read?

7 + 6 = 13   or   7 + 6 + 9 = 22

Strand: Number Strand Unit: Counting and numeration; Operations – addition
Strand: Measures Strand Unit: Length, Weight Skill: Problem-solving.

47

altogether ● add ● plus ● addition ● sum of ● how many? ● count on ● add on ● add up ● and ● total ● altogether ● add ● plus ● addition ● sum of ● how many? ● number sentence ● count on ● add up ● add ● and ● addition ● total ● altogether

10 Picture sums

Find the answers to the sums. Colour the picture according to the colour key.

Colour key

18 19 20 21

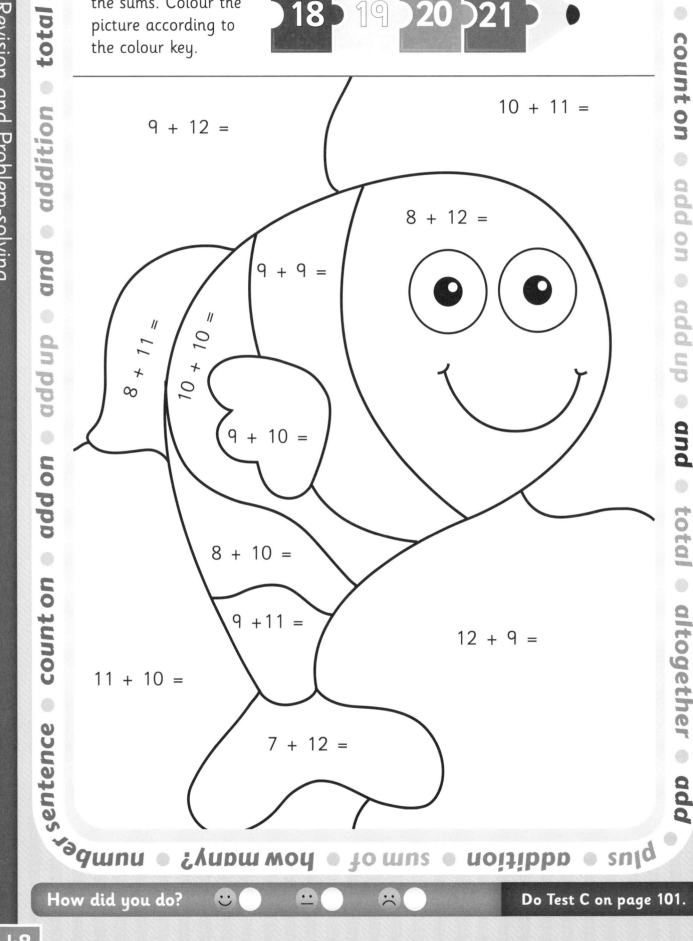

9 + 12 =

10 + 11 =

8 + 12 =

9 + 9 =

8 + 11 =

10 + 10 =

9 + 10 =

8 + 10 =

9 + 11 =

12 + 9 =

11 + 10 =

7 + 12 =

How did you do?   **Do Test C on page 101.**

Strand: Number **Strand Unit:** Counting and numeration; Operations – addition.

Subtract 1

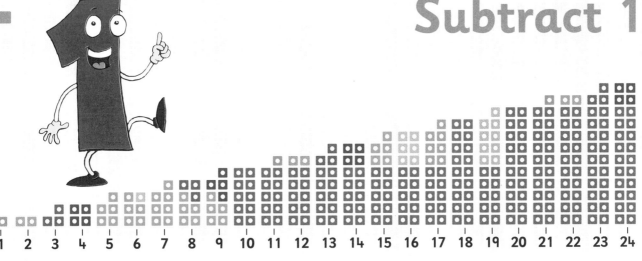

0 1 2 3 4 5 6 7 8 9 10 11 12 13 14 15 16 17 18 19 20 21 22 23 24

Monday

– 1 Tables

Monday	1 – 1 = 0		
	2 – 1 = 1		
	3 – 1 = 2		
	4 – 1 = 3		
	5 – 1 = 4		
	6 – 1 = 5		
Tuesday	7 – 1 = 6		
	8 – 1 = 7		
	9 – 1 = 8		
Wednesday	10 – 1 = 9		
	11 – 1 = 10		
	12 – 1 = 11		
	13 – 1 = 12		

Look

Say

Cover

Write

Check

Learn these

1 – 1 = 0
2 – 1 = 1
3 – 1 = 2
4 – 1 = 3
5 – 1 = 4

You try!

1 – 1 =
2 – 1 =
3 – 1 =
4 – 1 =
5 – 1 =

1 Take away

(a) 2 – 1 =

(b) 1 – 1 =

(c) 3 – 1 =

(d) 4 – 1 =

2 Colour the correct sum

(a)   –

| 3 + 1 = 4 | or | 3 – 1 = 2 | or | 4 – 1 = 3 |

(b)   –

| 4 – 1 = 3 | or | 5 – 1 = 4 | or | 5 – 5 = 0 |

3 Correct these. ✓ or ✗

(a) 3 – 1 = 2
(b) 1 – 1 = 0
(c) 2 – 1 = 1
(d) 4 – 1 = 5
(e) 5 – 1 = 4

Strand: Number **Strand Unit:** Counting and numeration; Operations – subtraction.

Tuesday

Learn these

6 – 1 = 5
7 – 1 = 6
8 – 1 = 7
9 – 1 = 8

You try!

6 – 1 =
7 – 1 =
8 – 1 =
9 – 1 =

1 Subtraction sums

(a) 7   (b) 9   (c) 8   (d) 5   (e) 1
    – 1   – 1   – 1   – 1   – 1
   ____   ____   ____   ____   ____

(f) 4   (g) 10   (h) 12   (i) 3   (j) 11
    – 1   – 1   – 1   – 1   – 1
   ____   ____   ____   ____   ____

2 Count back 1

(a) ← 5
(b) ← 8
(c) ← 7
(d) ← 6
(e) ← 4

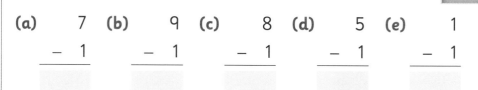

3 Take away

(a) 8 minus 1 =
(b) 5 minus 1 =
(c) 6 minus 1 =
(d) 7 minus 1 =
(e) 9 minus 1 =

Wednesday

Learn these

10 – 1 = 9
11 – 1 = 10
12 – 1 = 11
13 – 1 = 12

You try!

10 – 1 =
11 – 1 =
12 – 1 =
13 – 1 =

1 Fill in the missing numbers

(a) 11 –   = 10
(b)   – 1 = 12
(c) 10 –   = 9
(d)   – 1 = 11

2 + or – ?

(a) 9   1 = 10
(b) 11   1 = 10
(c) 12   1 = 13
(d) 10   1 = 9

3 Correct these. ✓ or ✗

(a) 12 – 1 = 11
(b) 10 – 1 = 9
(c) 9 – 1 = 10
(d) 11 – 1 = 10

4 Subtracting money

How much is left?

c

Strand: Number Strand Unit: Counting and numeration; Operations – subtraction
Strand: Measures Strand Unit: Money.

Thursday — Revision and Problem-solving

Learn these

1 – 1 =	0
2 – 1 =	1
3 – 1 =	2
4 – 1 =	3
5 – 1 =	4
6 – 1 =	5
7 – 1 =	6
8 – 1 =	7
9 – 1 =	8
10 – 1 =	9
11 – 1 =	10
12 – 1 =	11
13 – 1 =	12

Don't forget your... RUCSAC!

1 Problem-solving with tables

Colour each matching problem and sum the same colour. Write the answer.

(a) Louise has **3** cats. Oisín has **1** cat. How many **more** cats does Louise have than Oisín?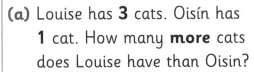

5 – 1 =

(b) Tim had **13** cent. He spent **1** cent. How much money does Tim have now?

3 – 1 =

(c) A lady bought **5** apples. She ate **1** apple. How many apples does she have now?

13 – 1 =

2 Colour 'yes' or 'no'

(a) 3 – 1 = 2
yes | no

(b) 1 – 1 = 2
yes | no

(c) 12 – 1 = 11
yes | no

(d) 10 – 1 = 9
yes | no

3 Subtraction words

Learn the words below. These words tell us to subtract.

minus	subtract	take away
difference	greater than	less than

Rough work

4 Test yourself!

2 – 1 =	8 – 1 =	10 – 1 =
12 – 1 =	1 – 1 =	5 – 1 =
3 – 1 =	7 – 1 =	6 – 1 =
9 – 1 =	11 – 1 =	
13 – 1 =	4 – 1 =	

My score ___ / 13

How did you do?

Strand: Number Strand Unit: Counting and numeration; Operations – subtraction
Strand: Measures Strand Unit: Money Skill: Problem-solving.

Do Test 13 on page 97. 51

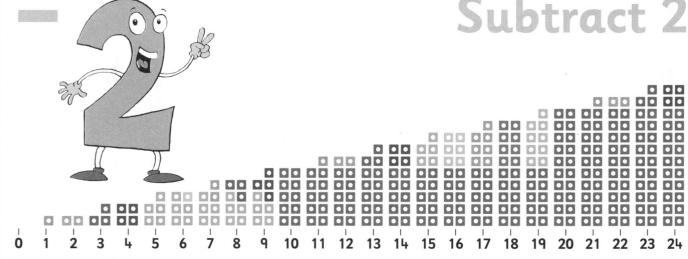

Subtract 2

Monday

– 2 Tables

Monday

2 – 2 = 0
3 – 2 = 1
4 – 2 = 2
5 – 2 = 3
6 – 2 = 4
7 – 2 = 5

Tuesday

8 – 2 = 6
9 – 2 = 7
10 – 2 = 8

Wednesday

11 – 2 = 9
12 – 2 = 10
13 – 2 = 11
14 – 2 = 12

Look

Say

Cover

Write

Check

Learn these

2 – 2 = 0
3 – 2 = 1
4 – 2 = 2
5 – 2 = 3
6 – 2 = 4

You try!

2 – 2 =
3 – 2 =
4 – 2 =
5 – 2 =
6 – 2 =

1 Subtract 2

Match each number with the correct answer.

– 2

3		5
7		1
10		4
12		8
8		6
6		0
9		7
2		9
11		10

2 Problem-solving with tables – pet shop

Don't forget your... RUCSAC!

Below are the animals in a pet shop. Answer the questions that follow.

(a) How many **more** snakes than cats?　　　3 – 1 = 2

(b) How many **more** snakes than frogs?

(c) How many **more** goldfish than mice?

(d) How many **more** snakes than mice?

(e) How many **more** goldfish than frogs?

Strand: Number **Strand Unit:** Counting and numeration; Operations – subtraction.

Tuesday

Learn these

7 – 2 = 5
8 – 2 = 6
9 – 2 = 7
10 – 2 = 8

You try!

7 – 2 =
8 – 2 =
9 – 2 =
10 – 2 =

1 Ring the correct answer

(a) 10 – 2 = 6 or 8

(b) 7 – 2 = 5 or 3

(c) 8 – 2 = 10 or 6

(d) 9 – 2 = 8 or 7

2 Count back 2

(a) ← 5   3   (b) ← 7

(c) ← 3   (d) ← 4

(e) ← 8   (f) ← 6

(g) ←12   (h) ← 2

3 Finish the number sentences

(a) 2 – 2 =

(b) 4 – 2 =

(c) 7 – 2 =

(d) 5 – 2 =

(e) 3 – 2 =

(f) 9 – 2 =

(g) 6 – 2 =

(h) 8 – 2 =

(i) 12 – 2 =

(j) 10 – 2 =

Wednesday

Learn these

11 – 2 = 9
12 – 2 = 10
13 – 2 = 11
14 – 2 = 12

You try!

11 – 2 =
12 – 2 =
13 – 2 =
14 – 2 =

1 Count back

     –

(a) 5 – 2 =

     –

(b) 7 – 2 =

2 Colour ✓ or ✗

(a) 13 – 2 = 11   ✓ ✗

(b) 10 – 2 = 8   ✓ ✗

(c) 12 – 2 = 14   ✓ ✗

(d) 11 – 2 = 9   ✓ ✗

(e) 14 – 2 = 10   ✓ ✗

3 Sums with brackets

(a) (6 – 2) + 2 =

(b) (9 – 2) + 7 =

(c) (11 – 2) – 0 =

(d) (12 – 2) – 6 =

(e) (10 – 2) – 2 =

Strand: Number Strand Unit: Counting and numeration; Operations – subtraction.

Thursday Revision and Problem-solving

Learn these

$2 - 2 = 0$
$3 - 2 = 1$
$4 - 2 = 2$
$5 - 2 = 3$
$6 - 2 = 4$
$7 - 2 = 5$
$8 - 2 = 6$
$9 - 2 = 7$
$10 - 2 = 8$
$11 - 2 = 9$
$12 - 2 = 10$
$13 - 2 = 11$
$14 - 2 = 12$

1 Colour the correct sum

(a)

| $5 - 2 = 3$ | or | $5 + 2 = 7$ | or | $7 - 2 = 5$ |

(b)

| $5 - 5 = 0$ | or | $3 - 2 = 1$ | or | $5 - 2 = 3$ |

2 + or – word?

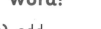

(a) add   +
(b) take away
(c) subtract
(d) altogether
(e) total
(f) difference
(g) minus

Rough work

3 Problem-solving with tables

Write a number sentence to match each problem.

(a) A bar costs **10** cent. A sweet costs **2** cent. How much **more** does the bar cost than the sweet?	$10 - 2 = 8$
(b) There were **8** children at Tina's party. **2** children went home. How many children are at Tina's party now?	
(c) A farmer has **11** sheep and **2** cows. How many **more** sheep than cows does he have?	
(d) Declan had **9** stickers. He lost **2**. How many stickers does he have now?	

4 Test yourself!

$2 - 2 =$	$8 - 2 =$	$10 - 2 =$
$12 - 2 =$	$14 - 2 =$	$5 - 2 =$
$3 - 2 =$	$7 - 2 =$	$6 - 2 =$
$9 - 2 =$	$11 - 2 =$	
$13 - 2 =$	$4 - 2 =$	

My score   / 13

How did you do?

Strand: Number Strand Unit: Counting and numeration; Operations – addition
Strand: Measures Unit: Money Strand Unit: Problem-solving.

Do Test 14 on page 97.

Subtract 3

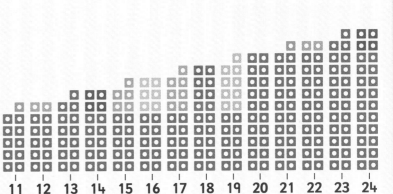

0 1 2 3 4 5 6 7 8 9 10 11 12 13 14 15 16 17 18 19 20 21 22 23 24

Monday

– 3 Tables

Monday	3 – 3 = 0
	4 – 3 = 1
	5 – 3 = 2
	6 – 3 = 3
	7 – 3 = 4
	8 – 3 = 5
Tuesday	9 – 3 = 6
	10 – 3 = 7
	11 – 3 = 8
	12 – 3 = 9
Wednesday	13 – 3 = 10
	14 – 3 = 11
	15 – 3 = 12

Look

Say

Cover

Write

Check

Learn these

3 – 3 = 0
4 – 3 = 1
5 – 3 = 2
6 – 3 = 3
7 – 3 = 4

You try!

3 – 3 =
4 – 3 =
5 – 3 =
6 – 3 =
7 – 3 =

1 Count back

(a)  – =

(b)  – =

(c)  – =

(d)  – =

(e)  – =

2 Subtracting money

(a)   minus

equals [ ] cent

(b)   take away

makes [ ] cent

(c) subtract

= [ ] cent

(d)   – [ ] [ ]

is the same as [ ] cent

Strand: Number **Strand Unit:** Counting and numeration; Operations – subtraction
Strand: Measures **Strand Unit:** Money.

Tuesday

Learn these

8 − 3 = 5
9 − 3 = 6
10 − 3 = 7
11 − 3 = 8

You try!

8 − 3 =

9 − 3 =

10 − 3 =

11 − 3 =

---

1 Subtraction sums

(a)
$$\begin{array}{r} 7 \\ -\ 3 \\ \hline \end{array}$$
(b)
$$\begin{array}{r} 5 \\ -\ 3 \\ \hline \end{array}$$
(c)
$$\begin{array}{r} 8 \\ -\ 3 \\ \hline \end{array}$$
(d)
$$\begin{array}{r} 6 \\ -\ 3 \\ \hline \end{array}$$
(e)
$$\begin{array}{r} 11 \\ -\ 3 \\ \hline \end{array}$$

(f)
$$\begin{array}{r} 3 \\ -\ 3 \\ \hline \end{array}$$
(g)
$$\begin{array}{r} 4 \\ -\ 3 \\ \hline \end{array}$$
(h)
$$\begin{array}{r} 10 \\ -\ 3 \\ \hline \end{array}$$
(i)
$$\begin{array}{r} 9 \\ -\ 3 \\ \hline \end{array}$$
(j)
$$\begin{array}{r} 12 \\ -\ 3 \\ \hline \end{array}$$

2 Fill in the missing numbers

(a) 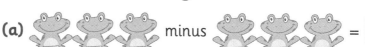 minus = frogs

(b)  minus flower =

(c) minus = pencils

Wednesday

Learn these

12 − 3 = 9
13 − 3 = 10
14 − 3 = 11
15 − 3 = 12

You try!

12 − 3 =

13 − 3 =

14 − 3 =

15 − 3 =

---

1 Fill in the missing numbers

(a) 12 − ___ = 9

(b) ___ − 3 = 12

(c) 13 − ___ = 10

(d) ___ − 3 = 11

2 + or − ?

(a) 13 ___ 3 = 10

(b) 11 ___ 3 = 8

(c) 15 ___ 3 = 12

(d) 10 ___ 3 = 13

3 Count back 3

(a) ← 15

(b) ← 12

(c) ← 14

(d) ← 13

(e) ← 10

(f) ← 11

4 Correct these. ✓ or ✗

(a) 12 − 3 = 9

(b) 14 − 3 = 17

(c) 11 − 3 = 8

(d) 6 − 3 = 9

(e) 13 − 3 = 16

Thursday Revision and Problem-solving

Learn these

3 – 3	=	0
4 – 3	=	1
5 – 3	=	2
6 – 3	=	3
7 – 3	=	4
8 – 3	=	5
9 – 3	=	6
10 – 3	=	7
11 – 3	=	8
12 – 3	=	9
13 – 3	=	10
14 – 3	=	11
15 – 3	=	12

1 Problem-solving with tables

Don't forget your... RUCSAC!

Colour each matching problem and sum the same colour. Write the answer.

(a) Adam had **10** cent. He spent **3** cent. How much money does Adam have now?

15 – 3 =

(b) Harriet had **15** marbles. She gave **3** marbles to her friend. How many marbles does Harriet have now?

7 – 7 =

(c) Ciara had **7** sweets. She ate **all** of her sweets! How many sweets does Ciara have now?

10 – 3 =

2 Subtract and draw

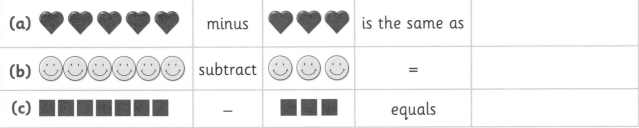

(a) ♥♥♥♥♥	minus	♥♥♥	is the same as	
(b) ☺☺☺☺☺☺	subtract	☺☺☺	=	
(c) ■■■■■■	–	■■■	equals	

Rough work

3 Test yourself!

13 – 3 =	8 – 3 =	10 – 3 =
12 – 3 =	14 – 3 =	5 – 3 =
3 – 3 =	7 – 3 =	6 – 3 =
9 – 3 =	11 – 3 =	
15 – 3 =	4 – 3 =	

My score ___ / 13

How did you do?

☺ ○
😐 ○
☹ ○

Strand: Number **Strand Unit:** Counting and numeration; Operations – subtraction
Strand: Measures **Strand Unit::** Money **Skill:** Problem-solving.

Do Test 15 on page 97.

57

Subtract 4

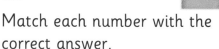

0 1 2 3 4 5 6 7 8 9 10 11 12 13 14 15 16 17 18 19 20 21 22 23 24

Monday

– 4 Tables

Monday	4 – 4 = 0
	5 – 4 = 1
	6 – 4 = 2
	7 – 4 = 3
	8 – 4 = 4
	9 – 4 = 5
Tuesday	10 – 4 = 6
	11 – 4 = 7
	12 – 4 = 8
	13 – 4 = 9
Wednesday	14 – 4 = 10
	15 – 4 = 11
	16 – 4 = 12

Look

Say

Cover

Write

Check

Learn these

4 – 4 = 0
5 – 4 = 1
6 – 4 = 2
7 – 4 = 3
8 – 4 = 4

You try!

4 – 4 =

5 – 4 =

6 – 4 =

7 – 4 =

8 – 4 =

1 Subtract 4

Match each number with the correct answer.

– 4

12		6
7		8
10		3
14		10
8		5
6		4
9		2
16		7
11		12

2 Fill in the missing numbers

(a) 5 – =

(b) 8 – =

(c) 6 – =

3 Minus 4

– 4

(a) 7

(b) 4

(c) 6

(d) 8

(e) 5

Strand: Number **Strand Unit:** Counting and numeration; Operations – subtraction.

Tuesday

Learn these

9 – 4 = 5
10 – 4 = 6
11 – 4 = 7
12 – 4 = 8

You try!

9 – 4 =
10 – 4 =
11 – 4 =
12 – 4 =

1 Finish the number sentences

(a) 5 – 4 =

(b) 15 – 4 =

(c) 9 – 4 =

(d) 6 – 4 =

(e) 7 – 4 =

(f) 16 – 4 =

(g) 4 – 4 =

(h) 14 – 4 =

(i) 12 – 4 =

(j) 10 – 4 =

2 Fill in the missing numbers

(a) 9 – = 5

(b) – 4 = 6

(c) 12 – = 8

(d) – 4 = 7

3 Correct these. ✓ or ✗

(a) 9 – 4 = 5

(b) 10 – 4 = 0

(c) 12 – 4 = 8

(d) 11 – 4 = 7

Wednesday

Learn these

13 – 4 = 9
14 – 4 = 10
15 – 4 = 11
16 – 4 = 12

You try!

13 – 4 =
14 – 4 =
15 – 4 =
16 – 4 =

1 + or – ?

(a) 9 4 = 13

(b) 11 4 = 7

(c) 12 4 = 16

(d) 10 4 = 6

(e) 15 4 = 11

3 Sums with brackets

(a) (7 – 4) + 2 =

(b) (5 – 4) + 4 =

(c) (11 – 4) – 3 =

(d) (12 – 4) – 4 =

2 Subtraction sums

(a) 9   (b) 12   (c) 5
   – 4   – 4   – 4
_____   _____   _____

(d) 11 (e) 16   (f) 4
   – 4   – 4   – 4
_____   _____   _____

(g) 14 (h) 7   (i) 8
   – 4   – 4   – 4
_____   _____   _____

Thursday Revision and Problem-solving

Learn these

$4 - 4 = 0$
$5 - 4 = 1$
$6 - 4 = 2$
$7 - 4 = 3$
$8 - 4 = 4$
$9 - 4 = 5$
$10 - 4 = 6$
$11 - 4 = 7$
$12 - 4 = 8$
$13 - 4 = 9$
$14 - 4 = 10$
$15 - 4 = 11$
$16 - 4 = 12$

Rough work

1 Subtracting money

(a)   take away   = ____ cent

(b) minus = ____ cent

2 Problem-solving with tables

Colour the sum that matches each problem.

(a) An apple costs **10** cent. A sweet costs **4** cent. How much **more** does the apple cost than the sweet?

| $10 - 4 = 6$ | or | $10 + 4 = 14$ |

(b) **14** children are playing hide-and-seek. **4** children have been found. How many children are still hiding?

| $14 - 0 = 14$ | or | $14 - 4 = 10$ |

(c) A bar costs **15** cent. A lollipop costs **4** cent. What is the **difference** in price between them?

| $15 - 4 = 11$ | or | $15 + 4 = 19$ |

3 Subtract and draw

(a) ⚽⚽⚽⚽⚽⚽	take away	⚽⚽⚽⚽	is the same as	
(b) ☺☺☺☺☺☺☺☺	subtract	☺☺☺☺	=	
(c) ■■■■■	–	■■■■	equals	

4 Test yourself!

$4 - 4 =$ $8 - 4 =$ $10 - 4 =$

$12 - 4 =$ $15 - 4 =$ $5 - 4 =$

$14 - 4 =$ $7 - 4 =$ $6 - 4 =$

$9 - 4 =$ $11 - 4 =$

$13 - 4 =$ $16 - 4 =$

How did you do?

My score [ ] / 13

Strand: Number **Strand Unit:** Counting and numeration; Operations – subtraction
Strand: Measures **Strand Unit:** Money **Skill:** Problem-solving.

Do Test 16 on page 97.

Revision and Problem-solving

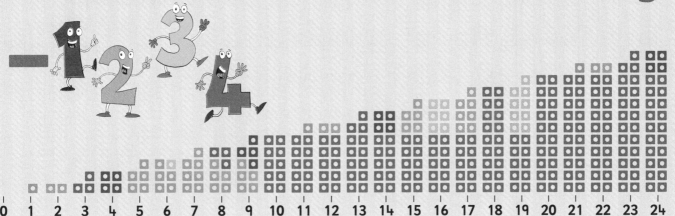

| 0 | 1 | 2 | 3 | 4 | 5 | 6 | 7 | 8 | 9 | 10 | 11 | 12 | 13 | 14 | 15 | 16 | 17 | 18 | 19 | 20 | 21 | 22 | 23 | 24 |

1 Test your memory!

Finish these number sentences.

(a) 6 – 1 =   (b) 8 – 3 =   (c) 5 – 2 =

(d) 7 – 4 =   (e) 9 – 1 =   (f) 4 – 4 =

(g) 2 – 2 =   (h) 10 – 1 =   (i) 12 – 3 =

(j) 8 – 2 =   (k) 11 – 4 =   (l) 12 – 1 =

(m) 7 – 2 =   (n) 8 – 4 =   (o) 11 – 1 =

(p) 9 – 2 =   (q) 3 – 3 =   (r) 12 – 4 =

2 Find the difference

(a) 4 – 2 =

(b) 6 – 3 =

3 Crack the code!

Complete the number sentences to crack the code.

5 – 1 =	**t**	9 – 3 =	**r**
8 – 3 =	**u**	2 – 2 =	**e**
10 – 2 =	**s**	11 – 4 =	**a**
12 – 3 =	**p**		

8	5	9	0	6		8	4	7	6

!

4 Fill in the missing numbers

(a)	9	(b)	12	(c)	9	(d)	9	(e)	7	(f)	7	(g)	10
	– 4		– ☐		– ☐		– 2		– ☐		– 3		– ☐
	☐		8		6		☐		5		☐		9

Strand: Number Strand Unit: Counting and numeration; Operations – subtraction.

5 Tricky sums

(a)   minus 2 = 5   (b)   subtract 4 = 1

(c)   take away 2 = 8   (d)   minus 3 = 0

(e)   subtract 2 = 6   (f)   take away 4 = 9

(g)   minus 1 = 10   (h)   subtract 3 = 4

7 What is missing?

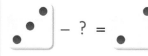

(a) 3 –   = 2   (b) 4 –   = 1

(c) 4 –   = 2   (d) 5 –   = 3

6 Subtract and match

Colour each matching sum and answer the same colour. Match them.

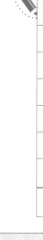

3 – 2	2
5 – 1	4
4 – 2	6
10 – 4	1
12 – 1	7
9 – 2	11
8 – 3	0
4 – 4	10
12 – 2	5
6 – 3	12
16 – 4	3

8 Sums with brackets

(a)   (4 – 4) + 2 =

(b)   (8 – 1) + 3 =

(c)   (6 – 3) + 4 =

(d)   (9 – 2) + 1 =

(e)   (11 – 2) + 1 =

(f)   (12 – 4) + 3 =

(g)   (1 – 0) + 2 =

Rough work

9 Problem-solving with tables

Colour the sum that matches each problem.

(a) Patrick cycled **8** kilometres. Zoe cycled **4** kilometres. How many **more** kilometres did Patrick cycle?

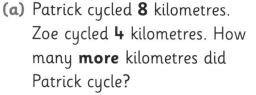

   8 + 4 = 12   or   8 – 4 = 4

(b) Tom's cat weighs **3** kilograms. Donna's dog weighs **6** kilograms. How much **heavier** is Donna's dog than Tom's cat?

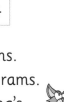

   6 – 3 = 3   or   3 + 6 = 9

(c) A farmer has **9** sheep and **5** cows. What is the **difference** between the number of cows and sheep that she has?

   9 – 5 = 4   or   4 + 5 = 9

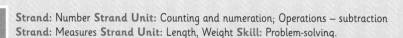

Strand: Number Strand Unit: Counting and numeration; Operations – subtraction
Strand: Measures Strand Unit: Length, Weight Skill: Problem-solving.

10 Picture sums

Find the answers to the sums. Colour the picture according to the colour key.

Colour key

4   5   6   7   8

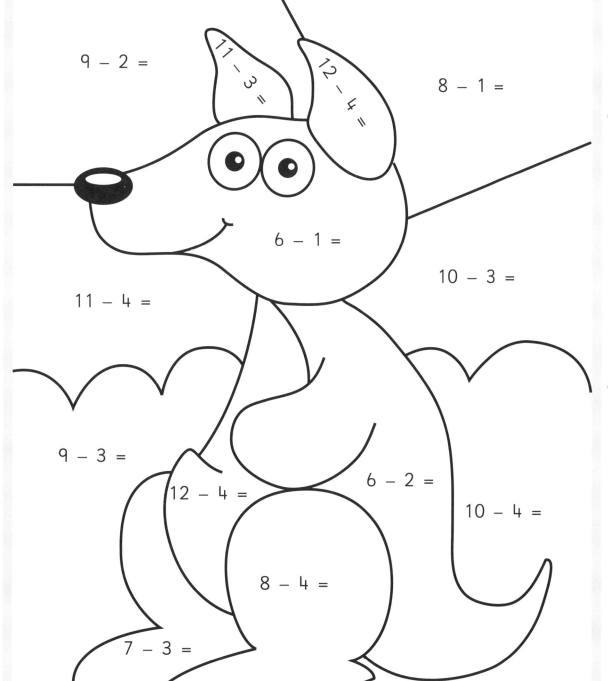

$11 - 3 =$

$12 - 4 =$

$9 - 2 =$

$8 - 1 =$

$6 - 1 =$

$10 - 3 =$

$11 - 4 =$

$9 - 3 =$

$12 - 4 =$

$6 - 2 =$

$10 - 4 =$

$8 - 4 =$

$7 - 3 =$

How did you do?   **Do Test D on page 101.**

Strand: Number **Strand Unit:** Counting and numeration; Operations – subtraction

Subtract 5

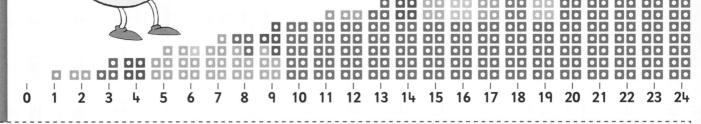

0 1 2 3 4 5 6 7 8 9 10 11 12 13 14 15 16 17 18 19 20 21 22 23 24

Monday

– 5 Tables

Monday				
5 – 5 =	0
6 – 5 =	1
7 – 5 =	2
8 – 5 =	3
9 – 5 =	4
10 – 5 =	5
11 – 5 =	6
12 – 5 =	7
13 – 5 =	8
14 – 5 =	9
15 – 5 =	10
16 – 5 =	11
17 – 5 =	12

Monday
Tuesday
Wednesday

Look

Say

Cover

Write

Check

Learn these

5 – 5 = 0
6 – 5 = 1
7 – 5 = 2
8 – 5 = 3
9 – 5 = 4

You try!

5 – 5 =

6 – 5 =

7 – 5 =

8 – 5 =

9 – 5 =

1 Take away

(a) 6 –  =

(b) 5 –  =

(c) 8 –  =

(d) 7 –  =

2 Colour the correct sum

(a)

| 6 – 5 = 1 | or | 6 – 6 = 0 | or | 6 – 1 = 5 |

(b)

| 8 – 3 = 5 | or | 8 – 4 = 4 | or | 8 – 5 = 3 |

3 Correct these. ✓ or ✗

(a) 7 – 5 = 2

(b) 8 – 5 = 3

(c) 9 – 5 = 1

(d) 10 – 5 = 5

(e) 11 – 5 = 4

Strand: Number **Strand Unit:** Counting and numeration; Operations – subtraction.

Tuesday

Learn these

10 – 5 = 5
11 – 5 = 6
12 – 5 = 7
13 – 5 = 8

You try!

10 – 5 =

11 – 5 =

12 – 5 =

13 – 5 =

1 Subtraction sums

(a)	6	(b)	9	(c)	8	(d)	7	(e)	11
	– 5		– 5		– 5		– 5		– 5

(f)	14	(g)	10	(h)	12	(i)	13	(j)	17
	– 5		– 5		– 5		– 5		– 5

2 Count back 5

(a) ← 10

(b) ← 12

(c) ← 13

(d) ← 11

(e) ← 8

3 Take away

(a) 10 minus 5 =

(b) 12 minus 5 =

(c) 13 minus 5 =

(d) 11 minus 5 =

(e) 9 minus 5 =

Wednesday

Learn these

14 – 5 = 9
15 – 5 = 10
16 – 5 = 11
17 – 5 = 12

You try!

14 – 5 =

15 – 5 =

16 – 5 =

17 – 5 =

1 Fill in the missing numbers

(a) 11 – ___ = 6

(b) ___ – 5 = 12

(c) 14 – ___ = 9

(d) ___ – 5 = 11

2 + or – ?

(a) 15 ___ 5 = 10

(b) 17 ___ 5 = 12

(c) 8 ___ 5 = 13

(d) 14 ___ 5 = 9

3 Correct these. ✓ or ✗

(a) 17 – 5 = 12

(b) 15 – 5 = 20

(c) 16 – 5 = 11

(d) 14 – 5 = 9

4 Subtracting money

How much is left?

c

Strand: Number Strand Unit: Counting and numeration; Operations – subtraction
Strand: Measures Strand Unit: Money.

65

Thursday Revision and Problem-solving

Learn these

5 – 5 = 0
6 – 5 = 1
7 – 5 = 2
8 – 5 = 3
9 – 5 = 4
10 – 5 = 5
11 – 5 = 6
12 – 5 = 7
13 – 5 = 8
14 – 5 = 9
15 – 5 = 10
16 – 5 = 11
17 – 5 = 12

❶ Problem-solving with tables

Colour each matching problem and sum the same colour. Write the answer.

(a) Alan bought **12** sweets in a shop. He ate **5** on the way home. How many sweets does Alan have now?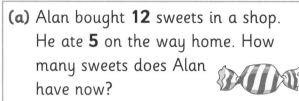

(b) Linda ran a race in **8** minutes. Jack ran the same race in **5** minutes. How many minutes **faster** was Jack's race time?

(c) Jennifer had **10** cent. She spent **half** of her money. How much money does Jennifer have now?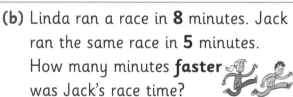

10 – 5 =

8 – 5 =

12 – 5 =

❷ Colour 'yes' or 'no'

(a) 15 – 5 = 10   yes no

(b) 5 – 5 = 5   yes no

(c) 12 – 5 = 7   yes no

(d) 10 – 5 = 5   yes no

❸ Ring the words that tell us to subtract

minus	subtract	altogether
difference	greater than	less than
add	total	take away

Rough work

❹ Test yourself!

5 – 5 =   8 – 5 =   10 – 5 =

12 – 5 =   17 – 5 =   15 – 5 =

14 – 5 =   7 – 5 =   6 – 5 =

9 – 5 =   11 – 5 =

13 – 5 =   16 – 5 =

My score / 13

How did you do?

Strand: Number Strand Unit: Counting and numeration; Operations – subtraction
Strand: Measures Strand Units: Time, Money Skill: Problem-solving.

Do Test 17 on page 98.

Subtract 6

0 1 2 3 4 5 6 7 8 9 10 11 12 13 14 15 16 17 18 19 20 21 22 23 24

Monday

– 6 Tables

Monday	6 – 6 = 0
	7 – 6 = 1
	8 – 6 = 2
	9 – 6 = 3
	10 – 6 = 4
	11 – 6 = 5
Tuesday	12 – 6 = 6
	13 – 6 = 7
	14 – 6 = 8
Wednesday	15 – 6 = 9
	16 – 6 = 10
	17 – 6 = 11
	18 – 6 = 12

Look

Say

Cover

Write

Check

Learn these

6 – 6 = 0
7 – 6 = 1
8 – 6 = 2
9 – 6 = 3
10 – 6 = 4

You try!

6 – 6 =

7 – 6 =

8 – 6 =

9 – 6 =

10 – 6 =

1 Subtract 6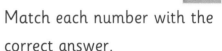

Match each number with the correct answer.

– 6

7	5
14	1
10	4
11	8
6	10
15	0
13	9
18	12
16	7

2 Problem-solving with tables – sweet shop

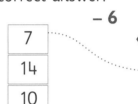

Below are the prices of sweets in a sweet shop. Answer the questions that follow.

 6c | 18c | 12c | 6c

(a) How much **more** does a candy cane cost than a sweet?

18 – 6 = 12

(b) How much **more** does a bun cost than a sweet?

(c) How much **more** does a candy cane cost than a lollipop?

(d) How much **more** does a bun cost than a lollipop?

(e) How much do a lollipop and a sweet cost **altogether**?

Strand: Number **Strand Unit:** Counting and numeration; Operations – addition
Strand: Measures **Strand Unit:** Money **Skill:** Problem-solving.

67

Tuesday

Learn these

11 – 6 = 5
12 – 6 = 6
13 – 6 = 7
14 – 6 = 8

You try!

11 – 6 =
12 – 6 =
13 – 6 =
14 – 6 =

1 Ring the correct answer

(a) 14 – 6 = 8 or 9

(b) 11 – 6 = 6 or 5

(c) 12 – 6 = 6 or 16

(d) 13 – 6 = 8 or 7

2 Count back 6

(a) ← 13   7   (b) ← 7

(c) ← 11   (d) ← 10

(e) ← 14   (f) ← 8

(g) ← 12   (h) ← 9

3 Finish the number sentences

(a) 14 – 6 =

(c) 7 – 6 =

(e) 13 – 6 =

(g) 6 – 6 =

(i) 12 – 6 =

(b) 18 – 6 =

(d) 15 – 6 =

(f) 9 – 6 =

(h) 8 – 6 =

(j) 10 – 6 =

Wednesday

Learn these

15 – 6 = 9
16 – 6 = 10
17 – 6 = 11
18 – 6 = 12

You try!

15 – 6 =
16 – 6 =
17 – 6 =
18 – 6 =

1 Count back

15 –

(a) 15 – 6 =

17 –

(b) 17 – 6 =

2 Colour ✓ or ✗

(a) 16 – 6 = 10   ✓ ✗

(b) 15 – 6 = 9   ✓ ✗

(c) 18 – 6 = 6   ✓ ✗

(d) 17 – 6 = 11   ✓ ✗

(e) 11 – 6 = 17   ✓ ✗

3 Sums with brackets

(a) (16 – 6) + 2 =

(b) (18 – 6) + 7 =

(c) (17 – 6) – 0 =

(d) (15 – 6) – 6 =

Strand: Number **Strand Unit:** Counting and numeration; Operations – subtraction.

Thursday Revision and Problem-solving

Learn these

$6 - 6 = 0$
$7 - 6 = 1$
$8 - 6 = 2$
$9 - 6 = 3$
$10 - 6 = 4$
$11 - 6 = 5$
$12 - 6 = 6$
$13 - 6 = 7$
$14 - 6 = 8$
$15 - 6 = 9$
$16 - 6 = 10$
$17 - 6 = 11$
$18 - 6 = 12$

1 Colour the correct sum

(a)

| $12 - 12 = 0$ or | $12 - 6 = 6$ or | $18 - 12 = 6$ |

(b)

| $15 - 6 = 9$ or | $16 - 6 = 10$ or | $10 - 6 = 4$ |

2 + or − word?

(a) minus   (b) take away   (c) total

(d) altogether   (e) subtract   (f) difference

(g) plus

3 Problem-solving with tables

Write a number sentence to match each problem.

Don't forget your... RUCSAC!

Problem	Number sentence
(a) A bar costs **17** cent. A sweet costs **6** cent. How much **more** does the bar cost than the sweet?	$17 - 6 = 11$
(b) There are **18** girls and **6** boys in Donna's class. How many **more** girls than boys are there in the class?	
(c) A farmer has **15** ducks and **6** hens. How many **more** ducks than hens does she have?	

Rough work

4 Test yourself!

$15 - 6 =$	$8 - 6 =$	$10 - 6 =$
$12 - 6 =$	$14 - 6 =$	$16 - 6 =$
$17 - 6 =$	$7 - 6 =$	$6 - 6 =$
$9 - 6 =$	$11 - 6 =$	
$13 - 6 =$	$18 - 6 =$	

How did you do?

My score   / 13

Strand: Number **Strand Unit:** Counting and numeration; Operations – subtraction
Strand: Measures **Strand Unit:** Money **Skill:** Problem-solving.

Do Test 18 on page 98.   69

Subtract 7

0 1 2 3 4 5 6 7 8 9 10 11 12 13 14 15 16 17 18 19 20 21 22 23 24

Monday

– 7 Tables

Monday
7 – 7	=	0
8 – 7	=	1
9 – 7	=	2
10 – 7	=	3
11 – 7	=	4

Tuesday
12 – 7	=	5
13 – 7	=	6
14 – 7	=	7
15 – 7	=	8
16 – 7	=	9

Wednesday
17 – 7	=	10
18 – 7	=	11
19 – 7	=	12

Look

Say

Cover

Write

Check

Learn these

7 – 7	=	0
8 – 7	=	1
9 – 7	=	2
10 – 7	=	3
11 – 7	=	4

You try!

7 – 7 =

8 – 7 =

9 – 7 =

10 – 7 =

11 – 7 =

1 Count back

(a) 7 – [dice] [dice] =

(b) 11 – [dice] [dice] =

(c) 10 – [dice] [dice] =

(d) 9 – [dice] [dice] =

(e) 8 – [dice] [dice] =

2 Subtracting money

(a)  take away

equals ____ cent

(b) [1 cent] minus [2 cent]

makes ____ cent

(c)  – [5 cent] [2 cent]

= ____ cent

(d)  [2 cent] [2 cent] minus [5 cent] [2 cent]

is the same as ____ cent

Strand: Number **Strand Unit:** Counting and numeration; Operations – subtraction
Strand: Measures **Strand Unit:** Money.

Tuesday

Learn these

12 – 7 = 5
13 – 7 = 6
14 – 7 = 7
15 – 7 = 8

You try!

12 – 7 =
13 – 7 =
14 – 7 =
15 – 7 =

1 Subtraction sums

(a) 7
 – 7

(b) 15
 – 7

(c) 8
 – 7

(d) 16
 – 7

(e) 11
 – 7

(f) 13
 – 7

(g) 10
 – 7

(h) 14
 – 7

(i) 9
 – 7

(j) 12
 – 7

2 Fill in the missing numbers

(a) 12 minus  = ____ frogs

(b) ____ flowers – 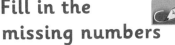 = 8 flowers

(c) 14 pencils –  = ____ pencils

---

Wednesday

Learn these

16 – 7 = 9
17 – 7 = 10
18 – 7 = 11
19 – 7 = 12

You try!

16 – 7 =
17 – 7 =
18 – 7 =
19 – 7 =

1 Fill in the missing numbers

(a) 16 – ____ = 9
(b) ____ – 7 = 12
(c) 13 – ____ = 6
(d) ____ – 7 = 11

2 + or – ?

(a) 17 ☐ 7 = 10
(b) 11 ☐ 7 = 18
(c) 15 ☐ 7 = 8
(d) 16 ☐ 7 = 9

3 Count back 7

(a) ← 16
(b) ← 18
(c) ← 19
(d) ← 17
(e) ← 15
(f) ← 13

4 Correct these. ✓ or ✗

(a) 16 – 7 = 9
(b) 18 – 7 = 12
(c) 19 – 7 = 10
(d) 17 – 7 = 11
(e) 15 – 7 = 8

Strand: Number Strand Unit: Counting and numeration; Operations – subtraction.

Thursday Revision and Problem-solving

Learn these

7 – 7 =	0
8 – 7 =	1
9 – 7 =	2
10 – 7 =	3
11 – 7 =	4
12 – 7 =	5
13 – 7 =	6
14 – 7 =	7
15 – 7 =	8
16 – 7 =	9
17 – 7 =	10
18 – 7 =	11
19 – 7 =	12

1 Problem-solving with tables

Colour each matching problem and sum the same colour. Write the answer.

(a) James has **12** sheep on his farm. Tom has **7** sheep on his farm. How many **more** sheep does James have than Tom?

(b) Tina has **19** cent. Sabrina has **7** cent. How much **more** money does Tina have than Sabrina?

(c) Brenda had **14** sweets. She ate **half** of them. How many sweets does Brenda have now?

14 – 7 =

12 – 7 =

19 – 7 =

2 Subtract and draw

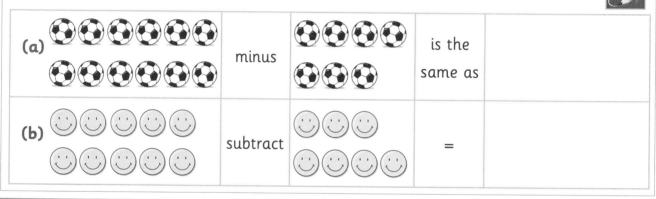

(a)		minus		is the same as
(b)		subtract		=

Rough work

3 Test yourself!

13 – 7 =	8 – 7 =	10 – 7 =
12 – 7 =	14 – 7 =	16 – 7 =
19 – 7 =	7 – 7 =	17 – 7 =
9 – 7 =	11 – 7 =	
15 – 7 =	18 – 7 =	

My score ___ / 13

How did you do?

Strand: Number **Strand Unit:** Counting and numeration; Operations – subtraction
Strand: Measures **Strand Unit:** Money **Skill:** Problem-solving.

Do Test 19 on page 98.

Subtract 8

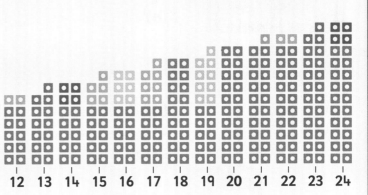

Monday

– 8 Tables

Monday	8 – 8 = 0
	9 – 8 = 1
	10 – 8 = 2
	11 – 8 = 3
	12 – 8 = 4
	13 – 8 = 5
Tuesday	14 – 8 = 6
	15 – 8 = 7
	16 – 8 = 8
Wednesday	17 – 8 = 9
	18 – 8 = 10
	19 – 8 = 11
	20 – 8 = 12

Look

Say

Cover
Write
Check

Learn these

8 – 8 = 0
9 – 8 = 1
10 – 8 = 2
11 – 8 = 3
12 – 8 = 4

You try!

8 – 8 =

9 – 8 =

10 – 8 =

11 – 8 =

12 – 8 =

1 Subtract 8

Match each number with the correct answer.

– 8

16	0
8	8
15	4
18	9
12	1
17	7
9	6
14	3
11	10

2 Fill in the missing numbers

(a) 12 –  =

(b) 8 –  =

(c) 10 –  =

3 Minus 8

– 8

(a)	9	1
(b)	12	
(c)	11	
(d)	10	
(e)	8	

Strand: Number **Strand Unit:** Counting and numeration; Operations – subtraction.

Tuesday

Learn these

13 – 8 = 5
14 – 8 = 6
15 – 8 = 7
16 – 8 = 8

You try!

13 – 8 =

14 – 8 =

15 – 8 =

16 – 8 =

1 Finish the number sentences

(a) 13 – 8 =　　　(b) 11 – 8 =　　　(c) 15 – 8 =

(d) 8 – 8 =　　　(e) 14 – 8 =　　　(f) 10 – 8 =

(g) 16 – 8 =　　　(h) 9 – 8 =　　　(i) 12 – 8 =

(j) 17 – 8 =

2 Fill in the missing numbers

(a) 13 –　　　= 5

(b)　　　– 8 = 6

(c) 16 –　　　= 8

(d)　　　– 8 = 7

3 Correct these. ✓ or ✗

(a) 16 – 8 = 8

(b) 14 – 8 = 0

(c) 15 – 8 = 7

(d) 13 – 8 = 6

Wednesday

Learn these

17 – 8 = 9
18 – 8 = 10
19 – 8 = 11
20 – 8 = 12

You try!

17 – 8 =

18 – 8 =

19 – 8 =

20 – 8 =

1 + or – ?

(a) 20　　　8 = 12

(b) 11　　　8 = 3

(c) 12　　　8 = 20

(d) 10　　　8 = 2

3 Sums with brackets

(a) (17 – 8) + 2 =

(b) (19 – 8) + 4 =

(c) (20 – 8) – 3 =

(d) (18 – 8) – 4 =

2 Subtraction sums

(a)	9	(b)	12	(c)	15
	– 8		– 8		– 8

(d)	11	(e)	16	(f)	17
	– 8		– 8		– 8

(g)	14	(h)	13	(i)	8
	– 8		– 8		– 8

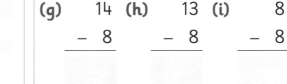

Strand: Number **Strand Unit:** Counting and numeration; Operations – subtraction.

Thursday | Revision and Problem-solving

Learn these

8	–	8	=	0
9	–	8	=	1
10	–	8	=	2
11	–	8	=	3
12	–	8	=	4
13	–	8	=	5
14	–	8	=	6
15	–	8	=	7
16	–	8	=	8
17	–	8	=	9
18	–	8	=	10
19	–	8	=	11
20	–	8	=	12

1 Subtracting money

(a)   –   = _____ cent

(b) minus   = _____ cent

2 Problem-solving with tables

Colour the sum that matches each problem.

(a) A spider has **eight** legs. A fly has **six** legs. How many **more** legs does a spider have than a fly?

$8 – 6 = 2$ or $8 + 6 = 14$

(b) A bar costs **15** cent. A lollipop costs **8** cent. What is the **difference** in price between them?

$8 + 15 = 23$ or $15 – 8 = 7$

Rough work

3 Subtract and draw

(a)	⚽⚽⚽⚽⚽⚽⚽⚽⚽⚽	take away	⚽⚽	=	
(b)	😊😊😊😊😊😊 😊😊😊😊😊😊	minus	😊😊 😊😊	=	
(c)	⬛⬛⬛⬛⬛⬛⬛⬛⬛	subtract	⬛	=	

4 Test yourself!

18 – 8 =	8 – 8 =	10 – 8 =
12 – 8 =	15 – 8 =	19 – 8 =
14 – 8 =	17 – 8 =	20 – 8 =
9 – 8 =	11 – 8 =	
13 – 8 =	16 – 8 =	

How did you do?

🙂 ◯
😐 ◯
🙁 ◯

My score [ ] / 13

Strand: Number **Strand Unit:** Counting and numeration; Operations – subtraction
Strand: Measures **Strand Unit:** Money **Skill:** Problem-solving.

Do Test 20 on page 98.

75

Revision and Problem-solving

0 1 2 3 4 5 6 7 8 9 10 11 12 13 14 15 16 17 18 19 20 21 22 23 24

---

1 Test your memory!

Finish these number sentences.

(a) 6 – 5 =

(b) 8 – 6 =

(c) 9 – 7 =

(d) 17 – 8 =

(e) 9 – 5 =

(f) 14 – 6 =

(g) 12 – 7 =

(h) 10 – 8 =

(i) 12 – 5 =

(j) 18 – 6 =

(k) 11 – 7 =

(l) 14 – 8 =

(m) 15 – 5 =

(n) 17 – 6 =

(o) 15 – 7 =

(p) 20 – 8 =

(q) 13 – 5 =

(r) 16 – 6 =

---

2 Find the difference

(a) 10 – 6 =

(b) 12 – 5 =

---

3 Crack the code!

Complete the number sentences to crack the code.

5 – 5 =	t	11 – 8 =	e
17 – 7 =	l	16 – 5 =	r
10 – 6 =	s	11 – 5 =	c
12 – 7 =	u	15 – 6 =	o
9 – 7 =	p	18 – 6 =	a

☐ ☐ ☐ ☐ ☐ ☐ ☐ ☐ ☐ ☐ !

4   2   3   6   0   12   6   5   10   12   11

---

4 Fill in the missing numbers

(a)   9   (b)   12   (c)   13   (d)   10   (e)   5   (f)   7   (g)   10
     – 5   – ☐   – ☐   – 8   – ☐   – 6   – ☐
    ☐   6   6   ☐   0   ☐   3

 Strand: Number **Strand Unit:** Counting and numeration Operations – subtraction.

5 Tricky sums

(a) ____ minus 6 = 5

(b) ____ subtract 8 = 11

(c) ____ take away 7 = 8

(d) ____ minus 5 = 0

(e) ____ subtract 5 = 8

(f) ____ take away 8 = 9

(g) ____ minus 7 = 10

(h) ____ subtract 6 = 4

7 What is missing?

(a) 12 – ____ = 6

(b) 8 – ____ = 3

(c) 10 – ____ = 2

(d) 12 – ____ = 5

6 Subtract and match

Colour each matching sum and answer the same colour. Match them.

13 – 5	7
15 – 6	9
14 – 7	2
10 – 8	8
12 – 8	3
9 – 6	0
8 – 7	6
14 – 8	4
16 – 5	1
6 – 6	11
19 – 7	12

8 Unscramble the sums

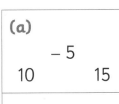

(a)
```
    – 5
10      15
```

(b)
```
    – 6
 3       9
```

(c)
```
     9
– 7      16
```

9 Problem-solving with tables

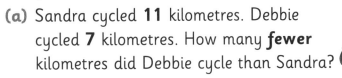

Colour the sum that matches each problem.

(a) Sandra cycled **11** kilometres. Debbie cycled **7** kilometres. How many **fewer** kilometres did Debbie cycle than Sandra?

11 – 7 = 4   or   11 + 7 = 18

(b) Emer read **12** pages of her book. Daniel read **8** pages of his book. How many **more** pages did Emer read than Daniel?

12 + 3 = 15   or   12 – 8 = 4

(c) A pet shop owner has **15** mice and **7** spiders. What is the **difference** between the number of mice and spiders?

15 + 7 = 22   or   15 – 7 = 8

Rough work

Strand: Number **Strand Unit:** Counting and numeration; Operations – subtraction
Strand: Measures **Strand Unit:** Length **Skill:** Problem-solving.

77

10 Picture sums

Find the answers to the sums. Colour the picture according to the colour key.

Colour key

  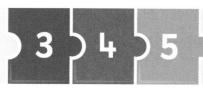

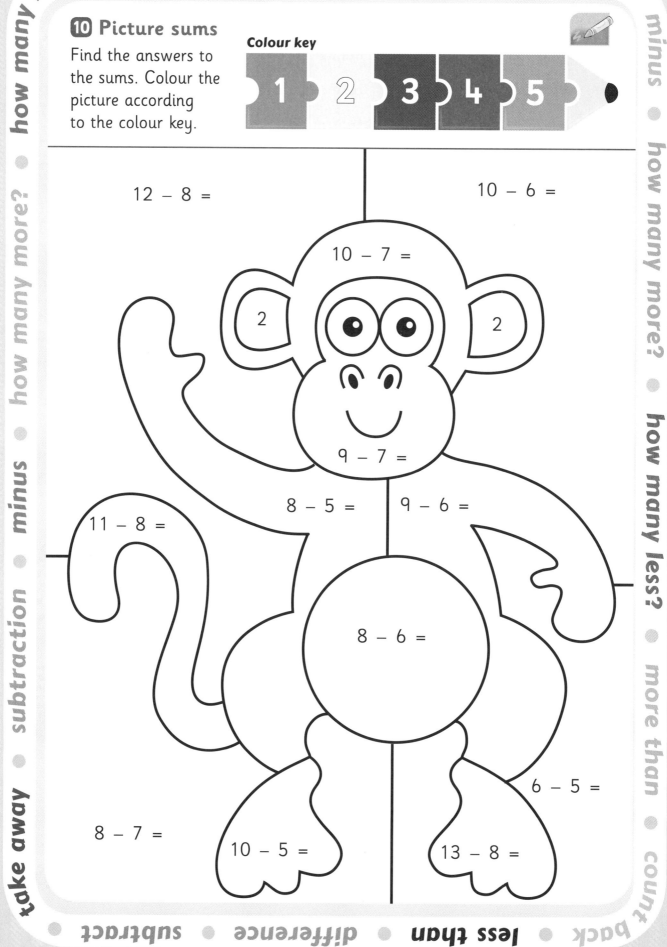

$12 - 8 =$

$10 - 6 =$

$10 - 7 =$

2

2

$9 - 7 =$

$8 - 5 =$

$9 - 6 =$

$11 - 8 =$

$8 - 6 =$

$6 - 5 =$

$8 - 7 =$

$10 - 5 =$

$13 - 8 =$

How did you do?   Do Test E on page 102.

78

Strand: Number **Strand Unit:** Counting and numeration; Operations – subtraction.

Subtract 9

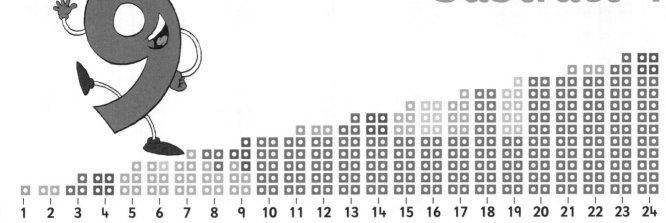

0 1 2 3 4 5 6 7 8 9 10 11 12 13 14 15 16 17 18 19 20 21 22 23 24

Monday

– 9 Tables

Monday	9 – 9 = 0
	10 – 9 = 1
	11 – 9 = 2
	12 – 9 = 3
	13 – 9 = 4
	14 – 9 = 5
Tuesday	15 – 9 = 6
	16 – 9 = 7
	17 – 9 = 8
	18 – 9 = 9
Wednesday	19 – 9 = 10
	20 – 9 = 11
	21 – 9 = 12

Look

Say

Cover

Write

Check

Learn these

9 – 9 = 0
10 – 9 = 1
11 – 9 = 2
12 – 9 = 3
13 – 9 = 4

You try!

9 – 9 =

10 – 9 =

11 – 9 =

12 – 9 =

13 – 9 =

1 Take away

(a) 12 – =

(b) 10 –  =

(c) 13 –  =

(d) 11 – =

2 Colour the correct sum

(a)

| 3 + 9 = 12 | or | 12 – 9 = 3 | or | 12 – 3 = 9 |

(b)

| 9 – 9 = 0 | or | 9 – 9 = 9 | or | 8 – 5 = 3 |

3 Correct these.
✓ or ✗

(a) 11 – 9 = 2

(b) 12 – 9 = 3

(c) 9 – 9 = 1

(d) 10 – 9 = 1

(e) 13 – 9 = 4

Tuesday

Learn these

14 − 9 = 5
15 − 9 = 6
16 − 9 = 7
17 − 9 = 8

You try!

14 − 9 =

15 − 9 =

16 − 9 =

17 − 9 =

1 Subtraction sums

(a) 16
    − 9

(b) 14
    − 9

(c) 15
    − 9

(d) 17
    − 9

(e) 11
    − 9

(f) 10
    − 9

(g) 12
    − 9

(h)   9
    − 9

(i) 13
    − 9

(j) 18
    − 9

2 Count back 9

(a) ← 14

(b) ← 17

(c) ← 16

(d) ← 15

(e) ← 13

3 Take away

(a) 17 minus 9 =

(b) 15 minus 9 =

(c) 14 minus 9 =

(d) 16 minus 9 =

(e) 12 minus 9 =

Wednesday

Learn these

18 − 9 = 9
19 − 9 = 10
20 − 9 = 11
21 − 9 = 12

You try!

18 − 9 =

19 − 9 =

20 − 9 =

21 − 9 =

1 Fill in the missing numbers

(a) 19 −   = 10

(b)   − 9 = 12

(c) 18 −   = 9

(d)   − 9 = 11

2 + or − ?

(a) 19   9 = 10

(b) 20   9 = 11

(c) 4   9 = 13

(d) 18   9 = 9

3 Correct these. ✓ or ✗

(a) 18 − 9 = 9

(b) 21 − 9 = 12

(c) 20 − 9 = 11

(d) 10 − 9 = 9

4 Subtracting money

How much is left?

 −

c

Strand: Number Strand Unit: Counting and numeration; Operations – subtraction
Strand: Measures Strand Unit: Money.

Thursday — Revision and Problem-solving

Learn these

9 – 9 = 0
10 – 9 = 1
11 – 9 = 2
12 – 9 = 3
13 – 9 = 4
14 – 9 = 5
15 – 9 = 6
16 – 9 = 7
17 – 9 = 8
18 – 9 = 9
19 – 9 = 10
20 – 9 = 11
21 – 9 = 12

1 Problem-solving with tables

Colour each matching problem and sum the same colour. Write the answer.

Don't forget your... RUCSAC!

(a) Shane bought **15** sweets. He gave **9** to his little brother. How many sweets does Shane have now?

(b) Jane ran a race in **21** minutes. Paul ran the race in **9** minutes. How many minutes **faster** was Paul's race time?

(c) Zoe had **18** cent. She spent **half** of her money. How much money does she have now?

21 – 9 =

18 – 9 =

15 – 9 =

2 Colour 'yes' or 'no'

(a) 19 – 9 = 10   yes   no

(b) 15 – 9 = 5   yes   no

(c) 12 – 9 = 3   yes   no

(d) 9 – 9 = 0   yes   no

3 Ring the words that tell us to subtract

plus   minus   difference

subtract   greater than   add

total   take away

Rough work

4 Test yourself!

18 – 9 =   20 – 9 =   10 – 9 =

12 – 9 =   17 – 9 =   15 – 9 =

14 – 9 =   19 – 9 =   21 – 9 =

9 – 9 =   11 – 9 =

13 – 9 =   16 – 9 =

My score ____ / 13

How did you do?

Strand: Number **Strand Unit:** Counting and numeration; Operations – subtraction
Strand: Measures **Strand Units:** Time, Money **Skill:** Problem-solving.

Do Test 21 on page 99.   81

Subtract 10

0 1 2 3 4 5 6 7 8 9 10 11 12 13 14 15 16 17 18 19 20 21 22 23 24

Monday

– 10 Tables

10 – 10 =	0
11 – 10 =	1
12 – 10 =	2
13 – 10 =	3
14 – 10 =	4
15 – 10 =	5
16 – 10 =	6
17 – 10 =	7
18 – 10 =	8
19 – 10 =	9
20 – 10 =	10
21 – 10 =	11
22 – 10 =	12

(left margin: Monday, Tuesday, Wednesday)

Look
Say
Cover
Write
Check

Learn these

10 – 10 =	0
11 – 10 =	1
12 – 10 =	2
13 – 10 =	3
14 – 10 =	4

You try!

10 – 10 =

11 – 10 =

12 – 10 =

13 – 10 =

14 – 10 =

1 Subtract 10

Match each number with the correct answer.

– 10

17	0
14	7
10	4
18	10
20	8
15	12
22	11
21	6
16	5

2 Problem-solving with tables – sweet shop

Below are the prices of sweets in a sweet shop. Answer the questions that follow.

 10c   22c   18c   10c

 RUCSAC! Don't forget your...

(a) How much **more** does a candy cane cost than a sweet?   22 – 10 = 12

(b) How much **more** does a bun cost than a sweet?

(c) How much **more** does a candy cane cost than a lollipop?

(d) How much **more** does a bun cost than a lollipop?

(e) How much do a lollipop and a bun cost **altogether**?

Strand: Number **Strand Unit:** Counting and numeration; Operations – subtraction
Strand: Measures **Strand Unit:** Money.

Tuesday

Learn these

15	– 10	=	5
16	– 10	=	6
17	– 10	=	7
18	– 10	=	8

You try!

15 – 10 =

16 – 10 =

17 – 10 =

18 – 10 =

1 Ring the correct answer

(a) 17 – 10 = 7 or 10

(b) 16 – 10 = 10 or 6

(c) 18 – 10 = 8 or 10

(d) 15 – 10 = 5 or 25

2 Count back 10

(a) ← 16   6   (b) ← 17

(c) ← 11   (d) ← 10

(e) ← 14   (f) ← 18

(g) ← 12   (h) ← 19

3 Finish the number sentences

(a) 14 – 10 =   (b) 18 – 10 =

(c) 17 – 10 =   (d) 15 – 10 =

(e) 13 – 10 =   (f) 19 – 10 =

(g) 16 – 10 =   (h) 22 – 10 =

(i) 12 – 10 =   (j) 10 – 10 =

Wednesday

Learn these

19	– 10	=	9
20	– 10	=	10
21	– 10	=	11
22	– 10	=	12

You try!

19 – 10 =

20 – 10 =

21 – 10 =

22 – 10 =

1 Count back

20 –

(a) 20 – 10 =

19 –

(b) 19 – 10 =

2 Colour ✓ or ✗

(a) 19 – 10 = 10   ✓ ✗

(b) 21 – 10 = 12   ✓ ✗

(c) 22 – 10 = 12   ✓ ✗

(d) 20 – 10 = 10   ✓ ✗

(e) 22 – 10 = 11   ✓ ✗

3 Sums with brackets

(a) (19 – 10) + 2 =

(b) (21 – 10) + 7 =

(c) (20 – 10) – 3 =

(d) (22 – 10) – 6 =

Strand: Number **Strand Unit:** Counting and numeration; Operations – subtraction.

Thursday Revision and Problem-solving

Learn these

10 – 10 = 0
11 – 10 = 1
12 – 10 = 2
13 – 10 = 3
14 – 10 = 4
15 – 10 = 5
16 – 10 = 6
17 – 10 = 7
18 – 10 = 8
19 – 10 = 9
20 – 10 = 10
21 – 10 = 11
22 – 10 = 12

1 Colour the correct sum

(a)

| 18 – 8 = 10 | or | 18 – 10 = 8 | or | 16 – 10 = 6 |

(b)

| 15 – 9 = 6 | or | 15 – 5 = 10 | or | 15 – 10 = 5 |

2 + or – word?

(a) minus   –

(b) take away

(c) total

(d) altogether

(e) subtract

(f) difference

(g) plus

Rough work

3 Problem-solving with tables

Write a number sentence to match each problem.

(a) A bar costs **22** cent. A lollipop costs **10** cent. What is the **difference** in price between them?	
(b) There are **18** girls and **10** boys in Emer's class. How many **more** girls than boys are there in the class?	
(c) A toy shop owner has **21** footballs and **10** dolls. How many **more** footballs than dolls does she have?	
(d) Jason had **19** stickers. He bought **10** more. How many stickers does Jason have now?	

4 Test yourself!

15 – 10 =   20 – 10 =   10 – 10 =

12 – 10 =   14 – 10 =   16 – 10 =

17 – 10 =   19 – 10 =   22 – 10 =

21 – 10 =   11 – 10 =

13 – 10 =   18 – 10 =

My score ____ / 13

How did you do?

Strand: Number **Strand Unit:** Counting and numeration; Operations – subtraction
Strand: Measures **Strand Unit:** Money **Skill:** Problem-solving.

Do Test 22 on page 99.

Subtract 11

0 1 2 3 4 5 6 7 8 9 10 11 12 13 14 15 16 17 18 19 20 21 22 23 24

Monday

– 11 Tables

Monday	11 – 11 = 0
	12 – 11 = 1
	13 – 11 = 2
	14 – 11 = 3
	15 – 11 = 4
	16 – 11 = 5
Tuesday	17 – 11 = 6
	18 – 11 = 7
	19 – 11 = 8
	20 – 11 = 9
Wednesday	21 – 11 = 10
	22 – 11 = 11
	23 – 11 = 12

Look

Say

Cover

Write

Check

Learn these

11 – 11 = 0
12 – 11 = 1
13 – 11 = 2
14 – 11 = 3
15 – 11 = 4

You try!

11 – 11 =

12 – 11 =

13 – 11 =

14 – 11 =

15 – 11 =

1 Count back

(a) 12 –  =

(b) 11 –  =

(c) 13 –  =

(d) 15 –  =

(e) 14 – =

2 Subtracting money

(a)   minus

equals _____ cent

(b)   minus

makes _____ cent

(c)   –

= _____ cent

(d)   –

is the same as _____ cent

Strand: Number **Strand Unit:** Counting and numeration; Operations – subtraction
Strand: Measures **Strand Unit:** Money.

85

Tuesday

Learn these

$16 - 11 = 5$
$17 - 11 = 6$
$18 - 11 = 7$
$19 - 11 = 8$

You try!

$16 - 11 =$

$17 - 11 =$

$18 - 11 =$

$19 - 11 =$

1 Subtraction sums

(a)	(b)	(c)	(d)	(e)
17	15	18	16	11
$- 11$	$- 11$	$- 11$	$- 11$	$- 11$

(f)	(g)	(h)	(i)	(j)
13	20	14	19	12
$- 11$	$- 11$	$- 11$	$- 11$	$- 11$

2 Fill in the missing numbers

(a) 19 frogs –  = ____ frogs

(b) 17 pencils –  = ____ pencils

Wednesday

Learn these

$20 - 11 = 9$
$21 - 11 = 10$
$22 - 11 = 11$
$23 - 11 = 12$

You try!

$20 - 11 =$

$21 - 11 =$

$22 - 11 =$

$23 - 11 =$

1 Fill in the missing numbers

(a) $20 - = 9$

(b) $ - 11 = 12$

(c) $21 - = 10$

(d) $ - 11 = 11$

2 + or – ?

(a) 17 ___ 11 = 6

(b) 11 ___ 11 = 22

(c) 15 ___ 11 = 4

(d) 16 ___ 11 = 5

(e) 12 ___ 11 = 23

3 Count back 11

(a) ← 20

(b) ← 22

(c) ← 21

(d) ← 23

(e) ← 19

(f) ← 16

4 Correct these. ✓ or ✗

(a) $22 - 11 = 11$

(b) $20 - 11 = 8$

(c) $23 - 11 = 12$

(d) $21 - 11 = 10$

Thursday Revision and Problem-solving

Learn these

11 – 11	=	0
12 – 11	=	1
13 – 11	=	2
14 – 11	=	3
15 – 11	=	4
16 – 11	=	5
17 – 11	=	6
18 – 11	=	7
19 – 11	=	8
20 – 11	=	9
21 – 11	=	10
22 – 11	=	11
23 – 11	=	12

1 Problem-solving with tables

Colour each matching problem and sum the same colour. Write the answer.

(a) Shane had **19** cent. He spent **11** cent. How much money does Shane have now?

15 – 11 =

(b) Barry had **15** marbles. He gave **11** marbles to his friend. How many marbles does Barry have now?

11 – 11 =

(c) Debbie had **11** sweets. She ate **all** of them! How many sweets does Debbie have now?

19 – 11 =

2 Subtract and draw

(a)		minus		=	
(b)		take away		=	

Rough work

3 Test yourself!

13 – 11 =	21 – 11 =	22 – 11 =
12 – 11 =	14 – 11 =	16 – 11 =
19 – 11 =	20 – 11 =	17 – 11 =
23 – 11 =	11 – 11 =	
15 – 11 =	18 – 11 =	

My score ___ / 13

How did you do?

Strand: Number **Strand Unit:** Counting and numeration; Operations – subtraction
Strand: Measures **Strand Unit:** Money **Skill:** Problem-solving.

Do Test 23 on page 99. 87

Subtract 12

0 1 2 3 4 5 6 7 8 9 10 11 12 13 14 15 16 17 18 19 20 21 22 23 24

Monday

– 12 Tables

Monday	12 – 12 = 0
	13 – 12 = 1
	14 – 12 = 2
	15 – 12 = 3
	16 – 12 = 4
	17 – 12 = 5
Tuesday	18 – 12 = 6
	19 – 12 = 7
	20 – 12 = 8
	21 – 12 = 9
Wednesday	22 – 12 = 10
	23 – 12 = 11
	24 – 12 = 12

Look

Say

Cover

Write

Check

Learn these

12 – 12 = 0
13 – 12 = 1
14 – 12 = 2
15 – 12 = 3
16 – 12 = 4

You try!

12 – 12 =

13 – 12 =

14 – 12 =

15 – 12 =

16 – 12 =

1 Subtract 12

Match each number with the correct answer.

– 12

16	3
13	4
15	1
12	0
22	8
17	10
20	2
14	12
24	5

2 Fill in the missing numbers

(a) 12 –  =

(b) 16 –  =

(c) 14 –  =

3 Minus 12

– 12

(a) 13   1

(b) 15

(c) 12

(d) 14

(e) 16

Strand: Number Strand Unit: Counting and numeration; Operations – subtraction.

Tuesday

Learn these

17	– 12	=	5
18	– 12	=	6
19	– 12	=	7
20	– 12	=	8

You try!

17 – 12 =

18 – 12 =

19 – 12 =

20 – 12 =

1 Finish the number sentences

(a) 13 – 12 =

(b) 20 – 12 =

(c) 15 – 12 =

(d) 18 – 12 =

(e) 14 – 12 =

(f) 17 – 12 =

(g) 16 – 12 =

(h) 19 – 12 =

(i) 12 – 12 =

(j) 22 – 12 =

2 Fill in the missing numbers

(a) 17 – ___ = 5

(b) ___ – 12 = 6

(c) 20 – ___ = 8

(d) ___ – 12 = 7

3 Correct these. ✓ or ✗

(a) 20 – 12 = 8

(b) 18 – 12 = 6

(c) 17 – 12 = 7

(d) 19 – 12 = 7

Wednesday

Learn these

21	– 12	=	9
22	– 12	=	10
23	– 12	=	11
24	– 12	=	12

You try!

21 – 12 =

22 – 12 =

23 – 12 =

24 – 12 =

1 + or – ?

(a) 20 ___ 12 = 8

(b) 12 ___ 12 = 24

(c) 22 ___ 12 = 10

(d) 24 ___ 12 = 12

(e) 11 ___ 12 = 23

3 Sums with brackets

(a) (20 – 12) + 2 =

(b) (24 – 12) + 4 =

(c) (22 – 12) – 3 =

(d) (23 – 12) – 4 =

2 Subtraction sums

(a)   20
    – 12
  _____

(b)   22
    – 12
  _____

(c)   24
    – 12
  _____

(d)   21
    – 12
  _____

(e)   19
    – 12
  _____

(f)   17
    – 12
  _____

(g)   14
    – 12
  _____

(h)   16
    – 12
  _____

(i)   18
    – 12
  _____

Strand: Number **Strand Unit:** Counting and numeration; Operations – subtraction.

Thursday Revision and Problem-solving

Learn these

12	– 12	=	0
13	– 12	=	1
14	– 12	=	2
15	– 12	=	3
16	– 12	=	4
17	– 12	=	5
18	– 12	=	6
19	– 12	=	7
20	– 12	=	8
21	– 12	=	9
22	– 12	=	10
23	– 12	=	11
24	– 12	=	12

Rough work

1 Subtracting money

(a)   –   =   cent

(b)  minus   =   cent

2 Problem-solving with tables

Colour the sum that matches each problem.

(a) By **how much** is twenty greater than twelve?

| 20 – 12 = 8 | or | 20 + 12 = 32 |

(b) A bar costs **24** cent. A lollipop costs **12** cent. What is the **difference** in price between them?

| 12 + 12 = 24 | or | 24 – 12 = 12 |

(c) There are twelve eggs in one dozen. How many eggs are there in **two dozen**?

| 12 + 12 = 24 | or | 12 – 12 = 0 |

3 Subtract and draw

| (a) |  | take away |  | = | |
| (b) |  | subtract |  | = | |

4 Test yourself!

18 – 12 =	22 – 12 =	21 – 12 =
12 – 12 =	15 – 12 =	19 – 12 =
14 – 12 =	17 – 12 =	20 – 12 =
23 – 12 =	24 – 12 =	
13 – 12 =	16 – 12 =	

My score   / 13

How did you do?

Strand: Number Strand Unit: Counting and numeration; Operations – subtraction
Strand: Measures Strand Unit: Money Skill: Problem-solving.

Do Test 24 on page 99.

Revision and Problem-solving

0 1 2 3 4 5 6 7 8 9 10 11 12 13 14 15 16 17 18 19 20 21 22 23 24

1 Test your memory!

Finish these number sentences.

(a) 16 − 9 =

(b) 18 − 10 =

(c) 15 − 11 =

(d) 17 − 12 =

(e) 9 − 9 =

(f) 14 − 10 =

(g) 12 − 11 =

(h) 22 − 12 =

(i) 12 − 9 =

(j) 21 − 10 =

(k) 11 − 11 =

(l) 13 − 12 =

(m) 17 − 9 =

(n) 19 − 10 =

(o) 14 − 11 =

(p) 21 − 12 =

(q) 13 − 9 =

(r) 14 − 9 =

2 Find the difference

(a) 12 − 10 =

(b) 11 − 11 =

3 Crack the code!

Complete the number sentences to crack the code.

15 − 9 =   c   11 − 9 =   e

17 − 12 =   l   20 − 10 =   k

10 − 10 =   d   18 − 11 =   u

12 − 9 =   n   19 − 11 =   o

6   8   0   2   7   3   5   8   6   10   2   0

4 Fill in the missing numbers

(a) 9   (b) 12   (c) 16   (d) 19   (e) 20   (f) 17   (g) 22
   − 9   −   −   − 12   −   − 10   −
   ____   ____   ____   ____   ____   ____   ____
              2   5   11   11

Strand: Number Strand Unit: Counting and numeration; Operations − subtraction.

5 Tricky sums

(a) ___ minus 9 = 5 (b) ___ subtract 12 = 11

(c) ___ take away 11 = 8 (d) ___ minus 11 = 0

(e) ___ subtract 9 = 8 (f) ___ take away 9 = 9

(g) ___ minus 10 = 10 (h) ___ subtract 10 = 4

7 What is missing?

(a) ___ − 12 = 6 (b) ___ − 9 = 3

(c) ___ − 10 = 2 (d) ___ − 11 = 4

6 Subtract and match

Colour each matching sum and answer the same colour. Match them.

13 − 9	5
15 − 10	3
14 − 11	8
20 − 12	4
21 − 9	9
19 − 10	7
18 − 11	12
14 − 12	2
20 − 9	6
20 − 10	10
17 − 11	11

8 Sums with brackets

(a) (14 − 9) + 2 =

(b) (20 − 10) + 3 =

(c) (16 − 11) + 4 =

(d) (19 − 12) + 1 =

(e) (11 − 9) + 1 =

(f) (12 − 10) + 3 =

(g) (15 − 11) + 2 =

Rough work

9 Problem-solving with tables

Colour the sum that matches each problem.

(a) Stephen has **14** books in his school bag. His brother has **10** books in his school bag. How many **more** books does Stephen have than his brother?

14 + 10 = 24 or 14 − 10 = 4

(b) Gerry drives **24km** to work. Sophie drives **12km** to work. How much farther does Gerry drive to work?

24 − 12 = 12 or 24 + 12 = 36

(c) A pet shop owner has **21** parrots and **12** canaries. What is the **difference** between the number of parrots and canaries?

12 + 12 = 24 or 21 − 12 = 9

Strand: Number Strand Unit: Counting and numeration; Operations – subtraction
Strand: Measures Strand Unit: Length Skill: Problem-solving.

subtract • take away • subtraction

10 Picture sums

Find the answers to the sums. Colour the picture according to the colour key.

Colour key

6 7 8 9

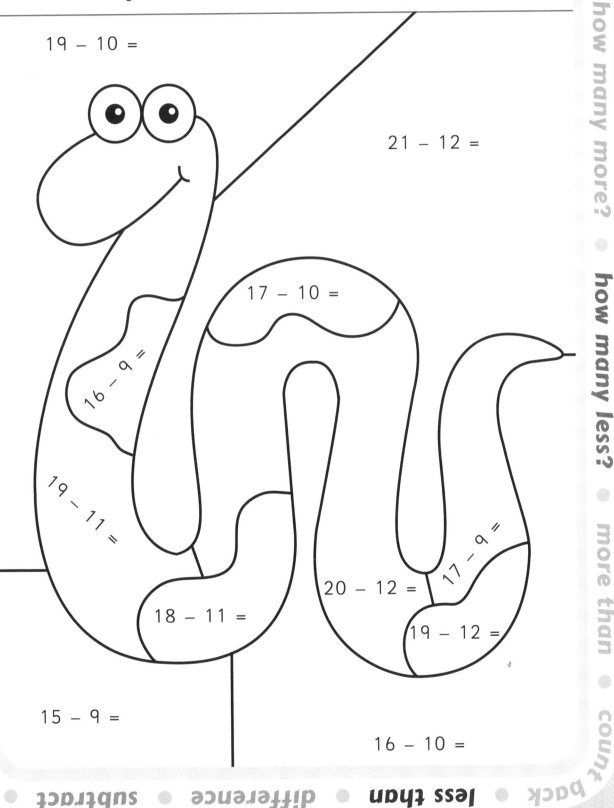

19 – 10 =

21 – 12 =

17 – 10 =

16 – 9 =

19 – 11 =

18 – 11 =

20 – 12 =

17 – 9 =

19 – 12 =

15 – 9 =

16 – 10 =

How did you do?   **Do Test F on page 102.**

Strand: Number **Strand Unit:** Counting and numeration; Operations – subtraction.

93

Friday Tests

Name:		Class:	
My time:		My score:	

Test 1	Test 2	Test 3	Test 4
+ 1 Tables	**+ 2 Tables**	**+ 3 Tables**	**+ 4 Tables**
(a) 5 + 1 =	(a) 2 + 2 =	(a) 6 + 3 =	(a) 12 + 4 =
(b) 8 + 1 =	(b) 7 + 2 =	(b) 12 + 3 =	(b) 0 + 4 =
(c) 1 + 1 =	(c) 10 + 2 =	(c) 0 + 3 =	(c) 2 + 4 =
(d) 6 + 1 =	(d) 3 + 2 =	(d) 2 + 3 =	(d) 7 + 4 =
(e) 12 + 1 =	(e) 11 + 2 =	(e) 5 + 3 =	(e) 10 + 4 =
(f) 0 + 1 =	(f) 4 + 2 =	(f) 8 + 3 =	(f) 3 + 4 =
(g) 2 + 1 =	(g) 9 + 2 =	(g) 1 + 3 =	(g) 11 + 4 =
(h) 7 + 1 =	(h) 5 + 2 =	(h) 7 + 3 =	(h) 5 + 4 =
(i) 10 + 1 =	(i) 8 + 2 =	(i) 10 + 3 =	(i) 8 + 4 =
(j) 3 + 1 =	(j) 1 + 2 =	(j) 3 + 3 =	(j) 1 + 4 =
(k) 11 + 1 =	(k) 6 + 2 =	(k) 11 + 3 =	(k) 6 + 4 =
(l) 4 + 1 =	(l) 12 + 2 =	(l) 4 + 3 =	(l) 4 + 4 =
(m) 9 + 1 =	(m) 0 + 2 =	(m) 9 + 3 =	(m) 9 + 4 =

Practise tables you need to learn again.

| Name: | | Class: | |

| My time: | | My score: | |

Test 5
+ 5 Tables

(a) 5 + 5 =

(b) 8 + 5 =

(c) 1 + 5 =

(d) 6 + 5 =

(e) 12 + 5 =

(f) 0 + 5 =

(g) 2 + 5 =

(h) 7 + 5 =

(i) 10 + 5 =

(j) 3 + 5 =

(k) 11 + 5 =

(l) 4 + 5 =

(m) 9 + 5 =

Test 6
+ 6 Tables

(a) 2 + 6 =

(b) 7 + 6 =

(c) 10 + 6 =

(d) 3 + 6 =

(e) 11 + 6 =

(f) 4 + 6 =

(g) 9 + 6 =

(h) 5 + 6 =

(i) 8 + 6 =

(j) 1 + 6 =

(k) 6 + 6 =

(l) 12 + 6 =

(m) 0 + 6 =

Test 7
+ 7 Tables

(a) 6 + 7 =

(b) 12 + 7 =

(c) 0 + 7 =

(d) 2 + 7 =

(e) 5 + 7 =

(f) 8 + 7 =

(g) 1 + 7 =

(h) 7 + 7 =

(i) 10 + 7 =

(j) 3 + 7 =

(k) 11 + 7 =

(l) 4 + 7 =

(m) 9 + 7 =

Test 8
+ 8 Tables

(a) 12 + 8 =

(b) 0 + 8 =

(c) 2 + 8 =

(d) 7 + 8 =

(e) 10 + 8 =

(f) 3 + 8 =

(g) 11 + 8 =

(h) 5 + 8 =

(i) 8 + 8 =

(j) 1 + 8 =

(k) 6 + 8 =

(l) 4 + 8 =

(m) 9 + 8 =

Practise tables you need to learn again.

Friday Tests

Name: _____ Class: _____

My time: _____ My score: _____

Test 9	Test 10	Test 11	Test 12
+ 9 Tables	**+ 10 Tables**	**+ 11 Tables**	**+ 12 Tables**
(a) 5 + 9 =	**(a)** 2 + 10 =	**(a)** 6 + 11 =	**(a)** 12 + 12 =
(b) 8 + 9 =	**(b)** 7 + 10 =	**(b)** 12 + 11 =	**(b)** 0 + 12 =
(c) 1 + 9 =	**(c)** 10 + 10 =	**(c)** 0 + 11 =	**(c)** 2 + 12 =
(d) 6 + 9 =	**(d)** 3 + 10 =	**(d)** 2 + 11 =	**(d)** 7 + 12 =
(e) 12 + 9 =	**(e)** 11 + 10 =	**(e)** 5 + 11 =	**(e)** 10 + 12 =
(f) 0 + 9 =	**(f)** 4 + 10 =	**(f)** 8 + 11 =	**(f)** 3 + 12 =
(g) 2 + 9 =	**(g)** 9 + 10 =	**(g)** 1 + 11 =	**(g)** 11 + 12 =
(h) 7 + 9 =	**(h)** 5 + 10 =	**(h)** 7 + 11 =	**(h)** 5 + 12 =
(i) 10 + 9 =	**(i)** 8 + 10 =	**(i)** 10 + 11 =	**(i)** 8 + 12 =
(j) 3 + 9 =	**(j)** 1 + 10 =	**(j)** 3 + 11 =	**(j)** 1 + 12 =
(k) 11 + 9 =	**(k)** 6 + 10 =	**(k)** 11 + 11 =	**(k)** 6 + 12 =
(l) 4 + 9 =	**(l)** 12 + 10 =	**(l)** 4 + 11 =	**(l)** 4 + 12 =
(m) 9 + 9 =	**(m)** 0 + 10 =	**(m)** 9 + 11 =	**(m)** 9 + 12 =

Practise tables you need to learn again.

Friday Tests

| Name: | | Class: | |

| My time: | | My score: | |

Test 13
– 1 Tables

(a) 5 – 1 =

(b) 8 – 1 =

(c) 1 – 1 =

(d) 6 – 1 =

(e) 12 – 1 =

(f) 13 – 1 =

(g) 2 – 1 =

(h) 7 – 1 =

(i) 10 – 1 =

(j) 3 – 1 =

(k) 11 – 1 =

(l) 4 – 1 =

(m) 9 – 1 =

Test 14
– 2 Tables

(a) 2 – 2 =

(b) 7 – 2 =

(c) 10 – 2 =

(d) 3 – 2 =

(e) 11 – 2 =

(f) 4 – 2 =

(g) 9 – 2 =

(h) 5 – 2 =

(i) 8 – 2 =

(j) 13 – 2 =

(k) 6 – 2 =

(l) 12 – 2 =

(m) 14 – 2 =

Test 15
– 3 Tables

(a) 6 – 3 =

(b) 12 – 3 =

(c) 13 – 3 =

(d) 15 – 3 =

(e) 5 – 3 =

(f) 8 – 3 =

(g) 14 – 3 =

(h) 7 – 3 =

(i) 10 – 3 =

(j) 3 – 3 =

(k) 11 – 3 =

(l) 4 – 3 =

(m) 9 – 3 =

Test 16
– 4 Tables

(a) 12 – 4 =

(b) 14 – 4 =

(c) 4 – 4 =

(d) 7 – 4 =

(e) 10 – 4 =

(f) 13 – 4 =

(g) 11 – 4 =

(h) 5 – 4 =

(i) 8 – 4 =

(j) 15 – 4 =

(k) 6 – 4 =

(l) 16 – 4 =

(m) 9 – 4 =

Practise tables you need to learn again.

Friday Tests

Friday Tests

Name: **Class:**

My time: **My score:**

Test 17	Test 18	Test 19	Test 20
– 5 Tables	**– 6 Tables**	**– 7 Tables**	**– 8 Tables**
(a) 5 – 5 =	(a) 13 – 6 =	(a) 14 – 7 =	(a) 12 – 8 =
(b) 8 – 5 =	(b) 7 – 6 =	(b) 12 – 7 =	(b) 14 – 8 =
(c) 13 – 5 =	(c) 10 – 6 =	(c) 15 – 7 =	(c) 16 – 8 =
(d) 6 – 5 =	(d) 14 – 6 =	(d) 13 – 7 =	(d) 13 – 8 =
(e) 12 – 5 =	(e) 11 – 6 =	(e) 18 – 7 =	(e) 10 – 8 =
(f) 14 – 5 =	(f) 15 – 6 =	(f) 8 – 7 =	(f) 15 – 8 =
(g) 16 – 5 =	(g) 9 – 6 =	(g) 17 – 7 =	(g) 11 – 8 =
(h) 7 – 5 =	(h) 16 – 6 =	(h) 7 – 7 =	(h) 17 – 8 =
(i) 10 – 5 =	(i) 8 – 6 =	(i) 10 – 7 =	(i) 8 – 8 =
(j) 15 – 5 =	(j) 17 – 6 =	(j) 16 – 7 =	(j) 20 – 8 =
(k) 11 – 5 =	(k) 6 – 6 =	(k) 11 – 7 =	(k) 18 – 8 =
(l) 17 – 5 =	(l) 12 – 6 =	(l) 19 – 7 =	(l) 19 – 8 =
(m) 9 – 5 =	(m) 18 – 6 =	(m) 9 – 7 =	(m) 9 – 8 =

Practise tables you need to learn again.

Friday Tests

Name:

Class:

My time:

My score:

Test 21	Test 22	Test 23	Test 24
– 9 Tables	**– 10 Tables**	**– 11 Tables**	**– 12 Tables**

Test 21 – 9 Tables

(a) $15 - 9 =$

(b) $18 - 9 =$

(c) $13 - 9 =$

(d) $16 - 9 =$

(e) $12 - 9 =$

(f) $14 - 9 =$

(g) $17 - 9 =$

(h) $19 - 9 =$

(i) $10 - 9 =$

(j) $20 - 9 =$

(k) $11 - 9 =$

(l) $21 - 9 =$

(m) $9 - 9 =$

Test 22 – 10 Tables

(a) $13 - 10 =$

(b) $15 - 10 =$

(c) $10 - 10 =$

(d) $16 - 10 =$

(e) $11 - 10 =$

(f) $14 - 10 =$

(g) $17 - 10 =$

(h) $22 - 10 =$

(i) $18 - 10 =$

(j) $19 - 10 =$

(k) $21 - 10 =$

(l) $12 - 10 =$

(m) $20 - 10 =$

Test 23 – 11 Tables

(a) $16 - 11 =$

(b) $12 - 11 =$

(c) $13 - 11 =$

(d) $18 - 11 =$

(e) $15 - 11 =$

(f) $20 - 11 =$

(g) $23 - 11 =$

(h) $17 - 11 =$

(i) $14 - 11 =$

(j) $19 - 11 =$

(k) $21 - 11 =$

(l) $11 - 11 =$

(m) $22 - 11 =$

Test 24 – 12 Tables

(a) $12 - 12 =$

(b) $20 - 12 =$

(c) $16 - 12 =$

(d) $18 - 12 =$

(e) $24 - 12 =$

(f) $13 - 12 =$

(g) $15 - 12 =$

(h) $19 - 12 =$

(i) $21 - 12 =$

(j) $17 - 12 =$

(k) $22 - 12 =$

(l) $14 - 12 =$

(m) $23 - 12 =$

Practise tables you need to learn again.

Revision Tests

Test A

1	2	3	4
(a) 8 + 1 =	(a) 4 + 3 =	(a) 12 + 3 =	(a) 9 + 2 =
(b) 11 + 1 =	(b) 6 + 2 =	(b) 2 + 1 =	(b) 0 + 2 =
(c) 5 + 2 =	(c) 12 + 4 =	(c) 2 + 4 =	(c) 8 + 2 =
(d) 7 + 4 =	(d) 10 + 4 =	(d) 3 + 2 =	(d) 0 + 3 =
(e) 5 + 3 =	(e) 8 + 3 =	(e) 5 + 1 =	(e) 4 + 4 =
(f) 1 + 2 =	(f) 2 + 2 =	(f) 2 + 3 =	(f) 1 + 3 =
(g) 1 + 1 =	(g) 11 + 2 =	(g) 11 + 4 =	(g) 10 + 1 =
(h) 5 + 4 =	(h) 12 + 2 =	(h) 1 + 4 =	(h) 6 + 4 =
(i) 3 + 1 =	(i) 8 + 4 =	(i) 4 + 2 =	(i) 10 + 3 =
(j) 7 + 1 =	(j) 6 + 3 =	(j) 12 + 1 =	(j) 3 + 4 =

My score _____ / 40 **How did you do?** 🙂 ⬤ 😐 ⬤ 🙁 ⬤

Test B

1	2	3	4
(a) 6 + 7 =	(a) 9 + 7 =	(a) 4 + 6 =	(a) 0 + 8 =
(b) 7 + 8 =	(b) 6 + 6 =	(b) 6 + 8 =	(b) 4 + 5 =
(c) 2 + 5 =	(c) 0 + 7 =	(c) 8 + 8 =	(c) 5 + 6 =
(d) 2 + 8 =	(d) 9 + 8 =	(d) 10 + 6 =	(d) 5 + 5 =
(e) 10 + 5 =	(e) 0 + 6 =	(e) 7 + 6 =	(e) 0 + 5 =
(f) 3 + 6 =	(f) 11 + 7 =	(f) 1 + 7 =	(f) 9 + 6 =
(g) 12 + 7 =	(g) 1 + 5 =	(g) 7 + 7 =	(g) 6 + 5 =
(h) 5 + 7 =	(h) 10 + 7 =	(h) 12 + 8 =	(h) 1 + 8 =
(i) 2 + 6 =	(i) 11 + 6 =	(i) 3 + 8 =	(i) 3 + 7 =
(j) 1 + 6 =	(j) 2 + 7 =	(j) 8 + 5 =	(j) 3 + 5 =

My score _____ / 40 **How did you do?**

Revision Tests

Test C

1	2	3	4
(a) 5 +11 =	(a) 4 + 9 =	(a) 3 +12 =	(a) 12 +10 =
(b) 5 +10 =	(b) 9 +11 =	(b) 3 + 9 =	(b) 7 +11 =
(c) 1 +12 =	(c) 1 + 9 =	(c) 0 +12 =	(c) 11 +12 =
(d) 7 +10 =	(d) 2 +12 =	(d) 12 + 9 =	(d) 6 + 9 =
(e) 9 +10 =	(e) 7 + 9 =	(e) 5 + 9 =	(e) 0 + 9 =
(f) 11 +10 =	(f) 11 +11 =	(f) 9 + 9 =	(f) 8 +11 =
(g) 11 + 9 =	(g) 3 +11 =	(g) 4 +12 =	(g) 2 +11 =
(h) 8 +10 =	(h) 2 + 9 =	(h) 0 +10 =	(h) 10 +10 =
(i) 4 +10 =	(i) 7 +12 =	(i) 10 +12 =	(i) 6 +11 =
(j) 12 +12 =	(j) 10 + 9 =	(j) 6 +12 =	(j) 2 +10 =

My score [   ] / 40   How did you do?

Test D

1	2	3	4
(a) 1 – 1 =	(a) 15 – 4 =	(a) 6 – 2 =	(a) 4 – 3 =
(b) 9 – 2 =	(b) 8 – 2 =	(b) 2 – 1 =	(b) 8 – 3 =
(c) 10 – 4 =	(c) 16 – 4 =	(c) 14 – 4 =	(c) 5 – 1 =
(d) 12 – 4 =	(d) 11 – 4 =	(d) 7 – 3 =	(d) 7 – 1 =
(e) 5 – 4 =	(e) 4 – 4 =	(e) 8 – 4 =	(e) 14 – 2 =
(f) 5 – 3 =	(f) 5 – 2 =	(f) 11 – 1 =	(f) 4 – 1 =
(g) 11 – 2 =	(g) 10 – 3 =	(g) 12 – 2 =	(g) 12 – 1 =
(h) 3 – 2 =	(h) 6 – 3 =	(h) 11 – 3 =	(h) 2 – 2 =
(i) 8 – 1 =	(i) 13 – 4 =	(i) 13 – 3 =	(i) 6 – 1 =
(j) 13 – 1 =	(j) 10 – 2 =	(j) 7 – 4 =	(j) 3 – 1 =

My score [   ] / 40   How did you do?

Revision Tests

Test E

1	2	3	4
(a) 16 – 8 =	(a) 9 – 5 =	(a) 7 – 7 =	(a) 10 – 8 =
(b) 7 – 6 =	(b) 9 – 8 =	(b) 13 – 6 =	(b) 12 – 7 =
(c) 12 – 6 =	(c) 12 – 8 =	(c) 11 – 6 =	(c) 11 – 8 =
(d) 18 – 7 =	(d) 9 – 7 =	(d) 18 – 8 =	(d) 15 – 6 =
(e) 6 – 6 =	(e) 13 – 8 =	(e) 17 – 7 =	(e) 17 – 8 =
(f) 19 – 7 =	(f) 10 – 6 =	(f) 18 – 6 =	(f) 17 – 6 =
(g) 10 – 7 =	(g) 15 – 7 =	(g) 13 – 7 =	(g) 9 – 6 =
(h) 14 – 7 =	(h) 14 – 6 =	(h) 8 – 8 =	(h) 16 – 6 =
(i) 16 – 7 =	(i) 14 – 8 =	(i) 19 – 8 =	(i) 8 – 7 =
(j) 8 – 6 =	(j) 15 – 8 =	(j) 11 – 7 =	(j) 20 – 8 =

My score [   ] / 40 **How did you do?**

Test F

1	2	3	4
(a) 16 – 11 =	(a) 12 – 10 =	(a) 16 – 10 =	(a) 12 – 11 =
(b) 22 – 12 =	(b) 20 – 9 =	(b) 17 – 11 =	(b) 23 – 11 =
(c) 17 – 12 =	(c) 18 – 12 =	(c) 18 – 9 =	(c) 14 – 10 =
(d) 24 – 12 =	(d) 14 – 11 =	(d) 13 – 10 =	(d) 23 – 12 =
(e) 15 – 10 =	(e) 12 – 12 =	(e) 15 – 11 =	(e) 20 – 12 =
(f) 22 – 10 =	(f) 11 – 10 =	(f) 11 – 11 =	(f) 13 – 11 =
(g) 21 – 11 =	(g) 18 – 11 =	(g) 17 – 10 =	(g) 21 – 10 =
(h) 19 – 12 =	(h) 21 – 12 =	(h) 20 – 10 =	(h) 22 – 11 =
(i) 10 – 9 =	(i) 13 – 12 =	(i) 19 – 11 =	(i) 18 – 10 =
(j) 15 – 12 =	(j) 14 – 12 =	(j) 19 – 10 =	(j) 16 – 12 =

My score [   ] / 40 **How did you do?**

Friday Test Results

Test 1

Date:

Results:

(a)
(b)
(c)
(d)
(e)
(f)
(g)
(h)
(i)
(j)
(k)
(l)
(m)

Test 2

Date:

Results:

(a)
(b)
(c)
(d)
(e)
(f)
(g)
(h)
(i)
(j)
(k)
(l)
(m)

Test 3

Date:

Results:

(a)
(b)
(c)
(d)
(e)
(f)
(g)
(h)
(i)
(j)
(k)
(l)
(m)

Test 4

Date:

Results:

(a)
(b)
(c)
(d)
(e)
(f)
(g)
(h)
(i)
(j)
(k)
(l)
(m)

Test 5

Date:

Results:

(a)
(b)
(c)
(d)
(e)
(f)
(g)
(h)
(i)
(j)
(k)
(l)
(m)

Test 6

Date:

Results:

(a)
(b)
(c)
(d)
(e)
(f)
(g)
(h)
(i)
(j)
(k)
(l)
(m)

Test 7

Date:

Results:

(a)
(b)
(c)
(d)
(e)
(f)
(g)
(h)
(i)
(j)
(k)
(l)
(m)

Test 8

Date:

Results:

(a)
(b)
(c)
(d)
(e)
(f)
(g)
(h)
(i)
(j)
(k)
(l)
(m)

Test 9

Date:

Results:

(a)
(b)
(c)
(d)
(e)
(f)
(g)
(h)
(i)
(j)
(k)
(l)
(m)

Test 10

Date:

Results:

(a)
(b)
(c)
(d)
(e)
(f)
(g)
(h)
(i)
(j)
(k)
(l)
(m)

Test 11

Date:

Results:

(a)
(b)
(c)
(d)
(e)
(f)
(g)
(h)
(i)
(j)
(k)
(l)
(m)

Test 12

Date:

Results:

(a)
(b)
(c)
(d)
(e)
(f)
(g)
(h)
(i)
(j)
(k)
(l)
(m)

Friday Test Results

Test 13

Date:

Results:

(a)
(b)
(c)
(d)
(e)
(f)
(g)
(h)
(i)
(j)
(k)
(l)
(m)

Test 14

Date:

Results:

(a)
(b)
(c)
(d)
(e)
(f)
(g)
(h)
(i)
(j)
(k)
(l)
(m)

Test 15

Date:

Results:

(a)
(b)
(c)
(d)
(e)
(f)
(g)
(h)
(i)
(j)
(k)
(l)
(m)

Test 16

Date:

Results:

(a)
(b)
(c)
(d)
(e)
(f)
(g)
(h)
(i)
(j)
(k)
(l)
(m)

Test 17

Date:

Results:

(a)
(b)
(c)
(d)
(e)
(f)
(g)
(h)
(i)
(j)
(k)
(l)
(m)

Test 18

Date:

Results:

(a)
(b)
(c)
(d)
(e)
(f)
(g)
(h)
(i)
(j)
(k)
(l)
(m)

Test 19

Date:

Results:

(a)
(b)
(c)
(d)
(e)
(f)
(g)
(h)
(i)
(j)
(k)
(l)
(m)

Test 20

Date:

Results:

(a)
(b)
(c)
(d)
(e)
(f)
(g)
(h)
(i)
(j)
(k)
(l)
(m)

Test 21

Date:

Results:

(a)
(b)
(c)
(d)
(e)
(f)
(g)
(h)
(i)
(j)
(k)
(l)
(m)

Test 22

Date:

Results:

(a)
(b)
(c)
(d)
(e)
(f)
(g)
(h)
(i)
(j)
(k)
(l)
(m)

Test 23

Date:

Results:

(a)
(b)
(c)
(d)
(e)
(f)
(g)
(h)
(i)
(j)
(k)
(l)
(m)

Test 24

Date:

Results:

(a)
(b)
(c)
(d)
(e)
(f)
(g)
(h)
(i)
(j)
(k)
(l)
(m)